# Fort Bridgewoods

**From Victorian Fort to WWII Y Station**

**(Palmerston's Enigma)**

**by**
**Stephen G Small, G4HJE**

Radio Society of Great Britain

Published by the Radio Society of Great Britain, 3 Abbey Court, Priory Business Park, Bedford, MK44 3WH United Kingdom
Tel: 01234 832700  Web: www.rsgb.org

First published 2015

Design and editing: Steve White, G3ZVW

Front cover:  Kevin Williams, M6CYB Production: Mark

Allgar, M1MPA

Printed by Latimer Trend & Comany Ltd of Plymouth

ISBN: 9781 9101 9309 9

# Contents

# Foreword

When one reads the many accounts of the German WWII Enigma cipher machine, great emphasis is placed upon the magnificent work undertaken at Bletchley Park (Station X) in breaking the code. The men and women involved in the code breaking have rightly received much acclaim, yet those who spent days and nights intercepting the material for decoding have, perhaps understandably, been given much less recognition. Joan Nicholls' book *England Needs You* does much to underline the dedicated work undertaken at Beaumanor and other outstations by many War Office Y Group men and women, both in the Services (ATS) and civilians (EWAs) who enabled those at Bletchley Park to be so successful in their endeavors.

Stephen Small has, by his initiative and interest in radio and Morse code, developed a fascinating account of Fort Bridgewoods from the time of Palmerston to its demise in the 1980s.

Without accurate intercept the task of code breaking at Bletchley Park would have been more difficult. The importance of Fort Bridgewoods as the birthplace of serious War Office intercept capabilities, and the training place of many civilian operators, has perhaps been neglected.

With the story of the Fort there are two additional elements - human and equipment. Stephen has covered these in great detail, with the story of Lt Commander Ellingworth, the Royal Navy trained instructors, and others. The inclusion of the basic radio receiver equipment in use at the Fort during both operational and training phases is also of much interest.

In my view *Fort Bridgewoods - From Victorian Fort to WWII Y Station* is an important contribution to the history of radio intercept, before and during WW2 at Fort Bridgewoods, and as a unique training place for civilian operators. Without this contribution there would be a void.

I am proud to have been involved in this work during the war and delighted to have been able to contribute material to develop the history of the Fort.

C N (Sandy) le Gassick, MBE
Lt Colonel, R.Signals

# Acknowledgements

I would not have been able to complete this book if it had not been for many very kind and generous people who have given me their support and access to their work, photographs and drawings, over which they have copyright.

Joan Nicholls, author of the excellent work *England Needs You*, has so very generously, and free of charge, given me her permission to make use of photographs and drawings from her work. In giving her permission Joan has asked me to specifically acknowledge Howard Jellings who, as a professional photographer, took the images of the Fort Bridgewoods Home Guard, Beaumanor Home Guard, ATS Teleprinter Operators at Chicksands and those of Cornwallis in the Beaumanor courtyard. Joan has also asked that I acknowledge ownership of the wedding photograph in which both Lt Col Ellingworth and the Reverend Donald Brand appear as belonging to Kay Staddon.

Philip Blenkinsop, whose father and two of his uncles served at some time at Fort Bridgewoods, Chicksands and Beaumanor, provided me with the wonderful photographs of Fort Bridgewoods taken just prior to its final demolition, and has very kindly given his permission for them to be used within my work. Philip still regrets having not taken more.

Robert Connelly, whose father, as a naval officer, served at Fort Bridgewoods, Chicksands and Beaumanor, has very kindly given me access to his father's photograph and the Chronicles of St Upid, over which he holds copyright. Robert has very kindly given his permission for his father's photograph to appear in my book and for the cartoon of OSEE (Officer Commanding – Lt Cdr Ellingworth), which appears opposite the contents page of the Chronicle, also to be used.

With cartoons in mind, I record my thanks to the late Hugh Skillen, author of the *Beaumanor Staff Magazine*, from which the cartoons 'Trunky Three Hats' and 'The European War' have been 'borrowed'. Whilst acknowledging the late Hugh Skillen it would be very wrong if I did not acknowledge the talent of the late Dick Wilkinson (Wilk), whose wonderful drawings first brought me face to face with Commander Ellingworth. I am sure that both of them would have supported my work and approved of my use of these items.

My profile of Commander Ellingworth would have been very dull had Malcolm Ellingworth, nephew of the man himself, not so generously given me access to his wonderful family photographs and given his gracious permission for me to include them within my book.

In producing the profile of Commander Ellingworth I had been mindful that I had not managed to locate of photograph of him as a naval officer. The various strands of my search for such a photograph had all come to nothing until I managed to locate Paul Caton, one of Commander Ellingworth's grandsons. Paul told me that his father, Michael Caton, was still alive and had just what I was looking for. Within three days I had received the most remarkable photograph of Lieutenant Ellingworth RN, resplendent in frock coat, sword and medals, with his beautiful bride Eleanor on their wedding day in 1920. I would like to record my special thanks to both Paul and his father for allowing me access to this wonderful photograph and for their gracious permission for it to be included in my work. Having located one grandson I was also contacted by Alex Beaumont, who very kindly provided additional information, including the fact that his father, Captain Thomas Hilliard Beaumont, had been a radio amateur and held the call G6HB.

Aubrey Stevens provided some wonderful photographs of his father and very kindly gave permission for them to be included, along with his father's unique handwritten history. Aubrey and Sandy Le Gassick provided me with wonderful photographs of the Maidstone

Grammar School First XI cricket team and of the DF station at Moulton, in which they both appear.

Mike Coleman has spent many years researching 'Y' work and without his early help and support I would have laboured much longer establishing the development of SIGINT techniques and the vital importance of this development at Fort Bridgewoods by Captain – later Major – Jolowicz and his CRR team. For his help and support I am extremely grateful.

Ken Carling, one of the silent operators, has very generously given me access to the many photographs that he has collected over the years. What is all the more important, Ken has added to each photograph a comment of who appears, where it was taken and when.

I would like to thank John Adams, a fellow radio amateur who I have known for many years, and his sister Sue Weaver, who facilitated an introduction to their mother Cynthia. Her father was 'Pop' Blundell, one of the five EWAs who opened Fort Bridgewoods for interception work in 1926. Cynthia very kindly told me her family story and has very graciously provided me with the personal photograph of her standing at her father's graveside, after she had made her peace with him.

I also wish to add my sincere thanks to Lionel John Beale of Falmouth and his daughter Heather, for allowing me into their respective homes on a wet March day in 2013 and giving me access to their extensive archive of family material.

When I commenced my search for the first commanding officer of interception work at Fort Bridgewoods all I had to go on was that he had died suddenly in 1934. After many false starts I found another small lead in a short pamphlet from Bletchley Park entitled *Funkers and Sparkers*. This identified him as a Lieutenant, but this did not get me too much further as I had no idea if that was a Royal Navy or an Army rank. All started to become clear after meeting Mrs Cynthia Adams, who was able to identify that her late father had attended the funeral of Lt Beale and that it had been at Fort Pitt Military Cemetery, which is located locally in Rochester. Research at the Royal School of Military Engineering revealed the plot records and gave me a full name, address, date of death and date of funeral. With these facts to hand I was able to apply for copies of birth, marriage and death certificates. I really thought that I had cracked this difficult nut, however, I then ground to a halt as further research did not reveal any local leads to follow. I came to the conclusion, rightly as it turned out, that the family had moved away. This was perhaps confirmed by the overgrown state of the grave which, thanks to the Adjutant at RSME Brompton, is now in proper order.

Some six months passed before I made any further progress and the search was at last over following receipt of an unexpected e-mail. This was precipitated by a post that I had left on the Kent History Forum. Heather had been trying to establish why her grandfather had been awarded an MBE, and had found the excellent Kent History Forum site. I had just what she was looking for.

It was a great privilege to stand in Heather's lounge and see lovingly displayed the sword and medals of Lieutenant Lionel Attwell Beale, the first commanding officer of the wireless interception station at Fort Bridgewoods. John and Heather, thank you for all your kindness, help and continued support.

Finally, I wish to thank Dr Philip Blenkinsop, who so kindly agreed to proof read my original text. Philip; your help and support has been invaluable and I cannot thank you enough for your time, effort and wisdom. My debt of gratitude to you is large and I hope this simple thank you goes some way to repaying all your efforts and kindness.

Stephen G Small, Chatham, 2014

# Dedication

Without the vital work of the civilian Experimental Wireless Assistants at Fort Bridgewoods the breaking of Enigma may not have happened.

This book is dedicated to those who pioneered 'secret wireless work' at Fort Bridgewoods and to all those from the 'silent operator family' who have been so kind and helpful in supporting my research into a world of secrets that they have kept for so long.

# Chapter 1.
# Introduction

This book is a true labour of love; love of not just local history but also a location of which I have been aware since a very early age, and a lifelong love of the science and art of radio communication.

Why *Fort Bridgewoods - From Victorian Fort to WWII Y Station*? Well, book titles need to be catchy, to entice the reader. More importantly for me though, it reflects the origins of the Chatham 'ring of steel'. The bracketed sub title *Palmerston's Enigma* refers to Lord Palmerston, who was responsible for building it, and the German secret high-grade machine code, Enigma, which was first intercepted by the staff of Fort Bridgewoods.

Local historians may argue that Lord Palmerston was almost a distant memory by the time that Fort Bridgewoods was completed, however, Lt Cdr Ellingworth when compiling his, at the time, 'Most Secret' unofficial history of War Office Y Group suggested that there existed an oral history that the Chatham forts were often referred to as Gladstone's folly, a play on Palmerston's follies which referred in general to the many south coast fortifications that were built as a result of the 1859 Royal Commission into the strategic defence of the South of England coastline.

It was the Royal Commission of 1859, set in train by Lord Palmerston, Prime Minister at the time, that set the War Office on a programme of fortification building to protect the all-important dockyard at Chatham, albeit after many years of Government prevarication and penny-pinching. Accordingly I have recognized the all-important initial involvement of Lord Palmerston by including him in the title for this book.

Enigma, whilst the given name for the commercial and subsequently military machine encryption system adopted by the German state in the 1930's, also suggests a secret that cannot be penetrated. Fort Bridgewoods was a place of many secrets and remained so until

# Fort Bridgewoods

it was finally demolished in the late 1980's. From the mid 1920's it disappeared from the Ordnance Survey and remained that way until it was finally abandoned.

The part that Fort Bridgewoods played in the development of wireless interception and traffic analysis was a vital one, indeed without the dedicated work and expert observations of the Experimental Wireless Assistants and intelligence officers at Fort Bridgewoods the cryptographers of Bletchley Park would not have had available to them the accurate signals material which enabled them to make the early 'breaks' into the German order of battle that in turn reduced the length of World War II by an estimated two years.

Whilst the Royal Commission of 1859 rightly identified the need to protect our coastline and the British fleet from a continental enemy, they could never have envisaged that one fort alone would play such a vital role in the development of what today is referred to as signals intelligence, and that in the dark days of World War II would prove so vital to eventual victory and delivering the free world from Hitler's tyrannical designs.

At times the narrative appears to be held up by insights into episodes of light relief as well as high drama, and it is hoped that the reader will both forgive and enjoy them for what they are.

# Chapter 2.
# Protecting the Fleet

On 21 October 1805 Admiral Lord Nelson and the British Fleet had won a glorious victory at Cape Trafalgar over the combined fleets of France and Spain. In the hundred years that followed the Royal Navy maintained supremacy of the high seas, thus protecting the trade routes of Empire and more importantly our ships of trade as they went about their lawful occasions. This was the age of '*Pax Britannica*'.

Ten years after Nelson's victory at Trafalgar, Napoleon's continental army was finally brought to a decisive battle at Waterloo by Lord Wellington and yet another great and glorious victory was had over the French. Whilst those in government surely hoped for a more settled Europe following the years of conflict, this was not to be. As Queen Victoria came to the throne in 1840 the power vacuum left following Napoleon's defeat had precipitated political unrest within continental Europe. This afforded the opportunity for posturing and power-play, which left the British Government uneasy about the future of European peace.

With an ever-expanding empire and continued dominance in world affairs, it became increasingly necessary to take all reasonable precautions to protect

**The Battle of Trafalgar.** © JMW Turner.

# Fort Bridgewoods

our vulnerable coastline - and most importantly our ability to maintain a foreign policy of 'gunboat diplomacy' by the protection of the Royal Navy and its anchorages and repair yards at Portsmouth and Chatham.

**The Dockyard at Chatham. © Richard Paton, 1793.**

A lesson in failing to protect the fleet and its anchorages had already been delivered in 1667 during the reign of Charles II. The Dutch fleet under the command of Admiral De Ruyter had sailed unhindered into the Medway estuary and on to Chatham, where they burnt the town and towed away the first rate HMS Royal Charles as a prize. For the Royal Navy, which had suffered badly under the stewardship of Oliver Cromwell, this was not to prove their finest hour. The fact that the Dutch admiral had been able to venture so close to London and the seat of government proved a severe embarrassment.

The Elizabethan castle at Upnor had proved wholly ineffectual in halting the Dutch fleet and there was much subsequent debate as to how to protect the fleet at its anchorage.

In 1756 Fort Amherst, with its complex of upper works, ditches and redoubts which occupies the high ground that overlooks the town of Chatham, was constructed to protect the dockyard and fleet anchorage. Further works were completed between 1805 and 1815, with the construction of Fort Pitt and Fort Clarence, which occupy the high ground on the Rochester side of the river. The fine period print made by William Miller depicts the view over the river from Fort Amherst and permits the viewer to imagine the arcs of fire for the guns. In the distance can be seen the corresponding fort, Fort Pitt, on the adjacent high ground which is now known as the Victoria Gardens and Jackson fields.

In 1859 a Royal Commission was established to consider The Defences of the United Kingdom, to which Major William Francis Drummond Jervois of the Royal Engineers was appointed as secretary. Jervois, born on 10 September 1821 at Cowes of a Huguenot family, entered military service at the Royal Military Academy at Woolwich. In March 1839 he was commissioned and gazetted as a second lieutenant in the Royal Engineers. The young Lieutenant Jervois found himself at the Royal School of Military Engineering at Chatham, where he received his initial training.

**The Royal Navy anchorage at Chatham, viewed from Fort Amherst. © William Miller, from drawings by JMW Turner.**

In 1841, having completed his formal training, he was promoted to Lieutenant and the following year was sent to South Africa where he distinguished himself as a Brigade Major, continuing his service there until his return to England in 1848.

Upon his return to England Jervois was appointed to command a company of Royal Engineers at Woolwich depot before being transferred with them to Guernsey. In 1850 he married Lucy and in the years that followed they were blessed with two sons and three daughters. By 1854 Jervois had risen to the rank of Major and the following year was appointed as Commanding Royal Engineer London District and as the Assistant Inspector General of Fortifications. His knowledge of fortification led to his subsequent appointment as secretary to the Royal Commission which was established on 20 August 1859 for the purpose of establishing the condition and efficiency of the existing land-based fortifications, for protecting key installations against naval operations from continental Europe. Specific emphasis was placed upon considering those fortifications that existed to protect the fleet and

**William Francis Drummond Jervois. © State Library of South Australia (B6984).**

anchorages at Chatham and the Medway, the Isle of Wight, Spithead, Portsmouth, Plymouth, Portland and Dover. The deliberation of the Commission was prompt, with a report being published on 7 February 1860. The Royal Commission of 1859 made specific recommendations for a ring of defensive fortifications around London, but the government of the day, in common with all governments, prevaricated over the high costs of such workings and in consequence none of the proposed works were adopted at the time.

Subsequently, a further government enquiry was commissioned under the title of the London Defence Scheme and in consequence a number of the recommendations from the

1859 Royal Commission were finally adopted. Jervois, as a respected Royal Engineer and acknowledged authority on the subject of protective fortification, went on to oversee the drawing-up of detailed designs for the workings that were derived from the London Defence Scheme. These workings were to become more commonly known as Palmerston Forts or, to the more cynical, Palmerston's Follies, most likely referring to the changing political vista that was continental Europe. By the time that work finally commenced on the building of the Chatham Ring of Steel, France had become our continental ally, although remaining a significant rivals in the race for naval supremacy, while Imperial Germany and Russia were beginning to dominate European political affairs.

**Plan drawing of the layout of Fort Borstal.**
**© HM Prison Rochester.**

Jervois prepared highly detailed drawings of the proposed forts, but further prevarication by government and arguments over mounting costs meant that he was to play no

# Fort Bridgewoods

**Front elevation of the Casemates at Fort Borstal.**
**© HM Prison Service.**

further part in the implementation of the building programme. By the mid 1860's Jervois had risen to senior rank and had been appointed to the colonies to review, inspect and advise upon matters of fortification. In 1882 he was promoted to Lieutenant General and served a term as Governor General in New Zealand. Lucy Jervois died in 1895 and two years later Jervois, at the age of 75, died from injuries sustained in a carriage accident. He is interred in the town of Virginia Water in Surrey.

The Royal Commission of 1859 had been highly critical of the significant lack of landward protection offered to the naval anchorage and dockyard at Chatham, yet government inaction and a culture of penny-pinching on the part of the Treasury meant that no significant action was taken to enhance the protection of the Royal Navy at Chatham.

By the mid-Victorian era a programme of expansion was found necessary, to ensure that Chatham Dockyard was able to cope with the developments in naval architecture and weapons technology. Although the Treasury had voted the funding for this project they continued to limit expenditure and, in consequence, the War Department and Admiralty were obliged to accept an insistence upon the use of convict labour for the expansion project.

**Chatham Public Works Convict Prison.**
**© HM Prison Service.**

In order to provide the necessary convict labour for the Chatham expansion project a new prison was established beyond St Mary's creek in 1856. The predominance of the officers appointed to the new public works convict prison were found from two prison hulks that were located in the Thames at Woolwich.

The convict prison proved to be a troubled place and although work on the dockyard extension employed some 500 or so convicts on a daily basis for hard manual labour, there was still an undercurrent of unrest and the opportunity for revolt against the prevailing conditions. Amongst the convict population at Chatham were a significant number of Fenians. Since the reign of Elizabeth I the Irish problem had festered and was again a prominent issue that taxed Queen Victoria's government. This mixture of poor conditions, harsh discipline and political unrest led to a potentially explosive mixture within the prison and frequent breakdowns in good order, an alarming number of escapes and even to mutiny.

A report in the *Kentish Gazette* dated Tuesday 26 February 1861 reports that on the previous Monday Major General Sir Joshua Jebb KCG, Inspector General of Pris-

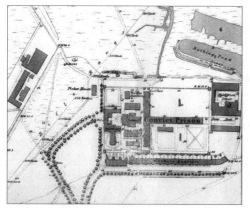

Map showing the Chatham Public Works Convict Prison. © HM Prison Service.

ons, accompanied by Captain Gambier, Director General of Convict Prisons, again visited the public works convict prison at Chatham, to continue their investigations into the then recent alarming outbreaks amongst convicts undergoing their sentence of penal servitude within the establishment. On his previous visit Sir Joshua had ordered that 48 prisoners, identified as ringleaders, be severely flogged and for a further 105 prisoners, who were deemed to have taken a prominent part in the recent revolt, be chained together and obliged to sleep at night on boards in the wash-house and bathrooms. The article also identifies that during the prisoners revolt and mutiny over £1000 worth of property had been destroyed. Consequently Jebb and Gambier were charged with establishing whether there existed cause for complaint by prisoners, and also whether recently laid down Home Office regulations and guidance to officers on the internal running of the prison and discipline of prisoners were being properly adhered to.

Recent disorder had been quelled by a force of 300 soldiers from the 1st Depot Battalion, under the command of Colonel Jervis. The soldiers, each armed with ten rounds of ball cartridge and with bayonets fixed, were to act against the convicts if required.

It was under these difficult circumstances that the extension of the dockyard was continued and a similar requirement by the Treasury was insisted upon when funds were finally released to the War Department for the building of forts to protect the inland approaches to the Dockyard. As with the dockyard extension project, a new public works convict prison was required. This was established on a hill just beyond the village of Borstal in 1877.

Unlike the convict prison at Chatham, which was demolished upon the completion of the dockyard extension to make land available for the new Royal Naval barracks, the prison at Borstal survives to this day, thanks to an innovative experiment in the treatment and rehabilitation of young offenders which was implemented in 1902 by the then Chairman of the Prisons Board, Sir Evelyn Ruggles-Brise. The village location also gave its name to the new penal system and it was, until 1983 when finally abandoned, known as Borstal Training. The convict prison completed, work on the forts could now commence.

The Gatelodge of HM Borstal, Rochester – the former public works convict prison. © HM Prison Service.

In 1872 the Treasury finally relented and removed the objections to the capital building project to provide landward protection for the dockyard at Chatham by means of a ring

# Fort Bridgewoods

of fortifications. Parcels of land were purchased on the basis of being 1.5 miles from the dockyard, reflecting the extreme range of the field guns of the day. In 1876 surveying began and the site and workings were finally pegged out. Work was started in 1877 on the overall building project, but suffered further delays and stoppages due to continuing issues over finance led by an intransigent Treasury.

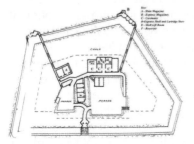

Two forts were to be built on the high ground just above the village of Borstal, with the objective of protecting the landward side of the Dockyard at Chatham and the first crossing point of the River Medway at Rochester. The sites chosen are about a mile outside Rochester, on land adjacent to the Rochester-Maidstone Road, what is now the B2097, which travels on to join the A229 as it makes its way towards Maidstone.

**Plan of Fort Bridgewoods when completed, 14 March 1892. © War Office, MoD 2014.**

Each fort was anticipated being built within five years and would require 600 men on a daily basis to achieve this objective. Correspondence between Godfrey Lushington, who subsequently became a Governor of Rochester Borstal, and Edward Du Cane of the Prison Department indicates that the figure of 600 prisoners was not a realistic one and indeed by 15 November 1882 it was more likely that only 405 prisoners could be deployed to the public works building project. Consequently the projection of a five year build period would have to be significantly extended. It was also noted that the prison at Borstal was operated independent of that at Chatham and consequently proposals were submitted for the building of an infirmary complex within the prison at a cost of £800. Correspondence between the Prison Department and the Treasury suggests that there was continued prevarication on the part of the Treasury. Although they finally relented and allocated funds, they then attempted to limit the

arrangements under which an additional eight temporary civil guards were employed. It was proposed that the eight additional guards receive a fixed salary of £60 per annum, which was significantly below the terms of existing staff. It was pointed out by Du Cane that this was not at all welcome by the prison authorities, who were already suffering powerful agitation from within the Prison Officer class for increases in pay and pension arrangements, and also for a reduction in their working week. It was suggested by Du Cane that rather than limit the remuneration arrangements for the eight temporary staff directly it should be left to the prison authorities to manage cost savings by not filling other vacancies. Indeed the attempt to make these temporary appointments on less favourable terms would provide no pecuniary advantage to Government.

**Cell block at Borstal Convict Prison. © HM Prison, Rochester.**

Work finally commenced in the 1880's, by which

**Gatelodge of Fort Bridgewoods.**
© Dr Philip Blenkinsop.

time the traditional arrangements which had been incorporated in the designs of Jervois were outdated and had been overtaken by advances in munitions and weapons technology. Design changes were necessary and the completed Fort Bridgewoods was significantly different from that envisaged in the original proposals contained in the Royal Commission report of 1860.

The final layout of Fort Bridgewoods was five sided, although it did not form a pentagon. The longest face was to the North and the main works were aligned East to West. The gateway was let into the centre of the longest face, at which point the moat was crossed by a rolling drawbridge which was capable of being retracted into a space below the heavily armoured double doors. Crossing arcs of fire to protect the main gateway were achieved from two angled flanking fighting chambers to the East and West of the main entrance doors. These were designed to provide fire support using the new technology of the Gatling gun, which had for its day an outstanding rate of continuous fire. The name of the fort is painted above the archway of the main gates, with the date of 1889 displayed below the letters VR (representing Victoria Regina, in whose reign the fort was constructed).

**Casemates at Fort Bridgewoods.**
© Graham French.

The fort was surrounded by a deep moat and was originally constructed with three counterscarp galleries. This was to be reduced to two, following the mining exercises of 1907. The moat was lined with concrete throughout its whole length.

As one entered through the main gates a link tunnel took you deeper into the workings and finally branched to give access to the two parade grounds. The concrete structures had been built on the surface and then covered with earth, to provide a dampening effect to incoming explosive rounds.

Accommodation was provided in a series of casemates, which were well protected by their thick concrete construction and earth banking. Similar construction techniques were used for the main magazine and ancillary storage rooms.

# Fort Bridgewoods

The other important feature of the radical final design was that it now presented a profile which made it difficult to observe from any distance. Changes in weapon technology led to Fort Bridgewoods not being gunned in the manner that was original envisaged. Instead, should the need arise, gunnery would be provided by the use of field artillery pieces which could be sited on the high points of the mounds provided by the earth covered casemates and other internal workings.

It was the deep and well protected inner features which were to prove all important when Fort Bridgewoods was selected as a Military Wireless Interception Station in 1925. At the height of The Blitz operators were to bless the names of Palmerston and Gladstone and to be thankful for their 'folly'.

Materials for the construction of the forts were delivered by water barge up and down the River Medway to a landing stage at Borstal, from where they were unloaded by convict labour into trucks that were hauled up the side of an inclined plane track way. At the top of the inclined plane they arrived at the edge of Fort Borstal and the start of the tramway which provided communication between Fort Borstal and the workings for Forts Bridgewoods, Horsted, and Luton. On aerial photographs of today one can still just see the outline of the tramway as it crossed from Fort Bridgewoods to Fort Horsted.

**Access tunnel to the two parade grounds.**
© Dr Philip Blenkinsop.

Oral history within the village of Borstal suggests that residents observed the tramway being operated by convict labour and this may well have been the case initially with convicts undertaking the heavy task of hauling the trucks by rope traces, much in the way that water barges were originally hauled by man power. By 1882 it is clear that mechanical propulsion was employed for hauling carriages along the tramway. This is evidenced in a letter written by an official of the Prison Department dated 11 October of that year, where he indicates that the passage of prisoners to and from the prison and the workings at Fort Horsted can be made with little risk in the covered and locked carriages running on the tramway by which they are connected.

In the early part of 1878 six experimental 'Handyside' locomotives were ordered by the War Office from Fox Walker and Co. They were of 2-4-2 wheel configuration and had an all-up weight of eight tons. The locomotives were initially tested at the Royal Arsenal at Woolwich in 1878 and by 1879 they had been transferred to the Royal Engineers at Brompton for field trials. The locomotives were found to be capable of 12mph on level ground and could negotiate curves of 15ft radius. The maximum haulage capacity was measured at 50 tons. Due to certain mechanical shortfalls they were rejected for commissioning for military combat work, but instead transferred to the War Office fort building project that was by now underway from Fort Borstal.

Aerial view of Rochester Airport and GEC Marconi, with Fort Bridgwoods in the top right corner. To the middle of the photograph can just be seen the remaining path of the light railway track way as it makes its way to Fort Horsted, which is just off the photograph bottom left. © GEC Marconi Ltd.

One of the buildings connected with the Borstal works tramway survived into the late 1990's and spent many years functioning as a cowshed, where Borstal Boys were gainfully employed. As many of the Borstal Boys at Rochester came from London, this was perhaps the first time that they had ever encountered a cow! The Borstal cowshed had, in its former life, been the engine workshop and one assumes would have provided shelter and security overnight for this important piece of machinery. Indeed, right up to the time when it was demolished, rails could still be seen running in the floor.

The cowshed at Rochester Borstal, which was originally the engine shed. © HM Prison, Rochester.

A recent discovery close to Fort Horsted is the remains of a tunnel which allows access to the fort under the existing roadway. Given the alignment of this tunnel and its size, it is reasonable to postulate that this was part of the tramway and allowed access to the Horsted site as the tramway made its way from Fort Bridgewoods.

# Fort Bridgewoods

Local oral history indicates that the tramway remained in operation until about 1905, which is consistent with the change of use of the prison establishment from convict prison to the first of the Borstal Training Institutions.

By the time of their completion the whole ring of forts could reasonably be said to be outdated and no longer fit for purpose, because techniques of defence and fighting had moved on with the swift advance of technology. Consequently the forts had very limited use as far as the military were concerned, but in 1907 the Royal Engineers conducted experimental mining operations whose outcomes were to provide serious lessons for the war with Germany, which by this time was looming.

**Handyside narrow gauge locomotive.**
© **Fox Walker and Co.**

Plans for the mining operations of 1907 can be found in the Royal Engineers Museum at Brompton. The object of the exercise was to undermine the moat of the fort, place explosive charges and then breach the moat in order to permit an assault by troops. A number of charges were exploded on days prior to the planned main assault in July of 1907, however, when the main charge was exploded it resulted in a clear breach and access to the fortifications for an attack by troops with bayonets fixed.

**1907 Mining Operations.**
© *Chatham Observer.*

The military mining operations were extensive and raised local interest, particularly when the large charges were detonated. So much so that the exercise, conducted by the Royal Engineers, was recorded by the *Chatham Observer*.

Despite the lack of real damage caused by the first day's charge, the second day's explosion clearly demonstrated the destructive power of the mining operations and the ability to breach fixed defences over a considerable distance, to permit a direct frontal assault by troops in the traditional manner with bayonets fixed. This would become all too familiar during operations to breach German front-line trenches in France and Belgium during World War I.

Following the mining operations of 1907 the breach in the moat was repaired, however, the counterscarp gallery that was destroyed in the exercise was not replaced. Despite the restoration work Fort Bridgewoods remained without garrison troops right up until the outbreak of World War I.

After the outbreak of World War I Fort Bridgewoods finally became home to regular troops when, in November 1914, a battalion of the Second Queen's Royal Regiment were ordered to Rochester. Upon their arrival the battalion was subdivided into companies, with

'A' company billeted at Fort Clarence and the remaining companies billeted in Forts Horsted, Borstal and Bridgewoods.

In May 1915 the battalion was formed-up on the land surrounding Fort Bridgewoods, where it camped under canvas. During this period the battalion headquarters was located within the Fort itself. They remained so camped until the autumn, when it was deemed prudent to relocate them back into the security of the forts.

**Borstal Boys working the land close to Fort Bridgewoods. © HM Prison, Rochester.**

Interestingly, the fields that surrounded Fort Bridgewoods were used by the prison department to provide gainful employment, training and a supply of food for the Borstal Boys, who now occupied the prison that had formerly housed the convict labour used to build the forts at Borstal, Bridgewoods and Horsted. The officers supervising, although dressed in plain clothes, could be clearly identified, as the Borstal Boys were dressed in short trousers and long socks reminiscent of a school uniform which indeed it was intended to replicate. The Borstal system drew heavily upon the public school system, with the cellblocks being known as houses, each house had a housemaster and a matron appointed to them. The houses at Rochester were for a long time all named after Admirals.

Records held at what is now Rochester Young Offenders Institution evidence that in the early years of the system the Borstal Boys were marched, by houses, to church on Sunday mornings, reflecting perhaps the importance at that time of religion as a part of the process of the boys' rehabilitation. Indeed the Chaplain and Medical Officer were second only to the Prison Governor when it came to the management of the establishment.

**Troops storming the breach, following the mining operation in 1907.**
**© *Chatham Observer*.**

Following the end of World War I, Fort Bridgewoods would have moved quietly into total obscurity had developments in technology and the advent of radio communications not loomed boldly over the horizon. The importance of signals intelligence had been quietly established at the height of World War I by shadowy figures, working initially for the Admiralty, whose lead in wireless interception and code breaking caused the establishment of the Government Code and Cypher School, under the ultimate direction of the Head of the Secret Service. By 1926 Fort Bridgewoods had moved from obscurity to being one of the most secret places in the realm.

# Chapter 3.
# Secrets of The Ether

In the late Victorian era experiments were being conducted into the potential to transmit information electronically and, what is more, without the use of wires. Both Tesla and Marconi had demonstrated the ability to transmit and receive signals over short distances using induction coils.

There had for many years been cable links which joined the United Kingdom with first the United States and thereafter the Empire. The first effective cable linking Great Britain with the United States had been laid down using the Brunel steamship the Great Eastern. Once established as a viable communications medium the cable system provided a revolutionary and speedy method of passing both government and commercial information between continents and seats of government using Morse code. With the communications of foreign powers having to pass through a central hub in England, it was not long before the Secret Service gained access to all the messages that traveled along the wires.

As the Empire mourned the passing of Queen Victoria radio experimenters continued to push the boundaries of wireless communication, but there remained a significant debate as to what medium permitted the movement of radio waves between two points. There had to be some invisible medium that supported their transmission. To explain the movement it was postulated that there existed such a medium and this was termed the 'Ether'. In 1908 Sir Oliver Lodge addressed the Royal Society in London in an attempt to define the substance of the Ether but, despite significant emerging research into the physics of the radiation and propagation of radio waves, the acceptance of a physical Ether continued to hold its own for many years to come.

It was not long before the military became interested in the science of radio and its potential as a weapon of war. The Royal Navy took a particular interest, as communicating with ships at sea had always been a long, drawn-out process, indeed it was the best part of a month before the Admiralty was made aware of Nelson's glorious victory over the combined French and Spanish fleet at Cape Trafalgar. The Admiralty encouraged experimental wireless work to be carried out by Captain Henry Jackson aboard the old wooden-wall HMS Defiance.

The development of wireless technology was fast joining the same race that all weapons development pursues, to assert the dominance of nations. Marconi, who had been quick to establish patents for his radio work, was clearly keen to develop the commercial potential of this emerging technology. The wonder of radio had also enthused the imagination of amateur experimenters and many of the significant breakthroughs in the science were achieved in humble back bedrooms and garden sheds, as opposed to well-appointed government or commercial research laboratories.

With the outbreak of World War I both Great Britain and Germany had access to wireless technology which, although still in its infancy, was to prove its value in providing quick and efficient battlefield communications. Radio communication, however, has one great flaw in its ability to be received by anyone with a suitable receiver. It is therefore open to friend and foe alike. The use of codes has been a feature of both military and civil life since the time of the Roman empire, and breaking codes has been a vital occupation for spies ever since.

Maurice Wright, father of former MI5 officer Peter Wright, who, it will be recalled, is the author of the infamous book *Spycatcher* that Prime Minister Margaret Thatcher attempted to suppress, joined the Marconi Company directly from University in 1912. In collaboration with Captain Henry Joseph Round he developed a receiver using a vacuum valve of their own design, which was to make long-range interception of radio signals possible for the first time. Round is perhaps the better remembered of the two, but the contribution of Maurice Wright was equally significant.

In the days leading up to the outbreak of World War I, Maurice Wright had been working with one of the experimental receivers and quickly established that what he was receiving in his laboratory, located in Hall Street, Chelmsford, were indeed German naval messages. With pen and paper to hand he quickly took down the information that was being received and, with a batch of handwritten notes in hand, he went off to find Andrew Gray, the Marconi Company works manager.

**Captain Henry Joseph Round.**
© Marconi Company Ltd.

**The vacuum valve developed by Captain Round.**
© Marconi Company Ltd.

## Fort Bridgewoods

Andrew Gray was a personal friend of Captain Reginald 'Blinker' Hall RN, who at the time was Head of the Naval Intelligence Department. Captain Hall was to be a pivotal player in the development of signals intelligence and code-breaking as the war progressed. He is, of course, famously remembered for being responsible for the attacks on German book codes with the small team of specialists who occupied Room 40 at Old Admiralty Building.

With his intercepted messages still in hand, it was arranged for Maurice Wright to travel directly to Liverpool Street station on the footplate of a specially chartered locomotive and from there he was quickly transported to the Admiralty, where he presented his treasure to Captain Hall. The significance of the intercepted messages and the ability to receive the signals from the East Coast was not lost on Hall and he promptly approached Marconi to ask for Wright to be released to Naval Intelligence in order to develop interception and direction finding stations for the Royal Navy.

**The receiver circuit developed by Captain Round and Maurice Wright, which used the newly developed Round valve. © Marconi Company Ltd.**

Hall and the Admiralty were acutely aware that, for the British Fleet at Scapa Flow to be able to counter the German High Seas Fleet, they needed to be able to have prior warning of its movement into the Kiel Canal and thereafter into the North Sea. Hall postulated that, with the developments of Wright and Round in wireless interception, the wireless communications of the German Admiral could be intercepted and the movement of the High Seas Fleet detected at an early enough time to enable to the British Fleet to sail and gain a tactical advantage. It would also prevent the need for expensive standing patrols being mounted by the Royal Navy, a tactic that was not lost on Air Marshall Hugh Dowding some twenty-five years later as he developed the tactics for fighting the Battle of Britain.

Wright went on to design and develop sensitive receivers and was to establish the process of 'aperiodic' direction finding, which permitted the bearing of a particular station's signal to be accurately identified amongst the many other signals that occupied that particular part of the air waves. Although it took several years to be made fully operational it became a vital tool in dealing with the menace of the German U Boats. The system of 'aperiodic' direction finding remains the process for all direction finding and was equally important during World War II in countering the U Boat menace during the Battle of the Atlantic.

**Maurice Wright's receiver. © Marconi Company Ltd.**

Wright also ran a successful six-month clandestine direction finding operation from the attic of a house in

Oslo. The MI6 station located within the British Embassy, provided Wright with a communication chain back to the Admiralty, as well as necessary equipment spares. He continued to provide much needed intelligence on the intentions of the German High Seas Fleet until one morning over breakfast he became aware of wanted posters which carried his picture and a reward for his capture. Having coolly finished his breakfast he collected up all evidence of his work and made good his escape, finally meeting up with a British naval officer who saw him safely aboard a waiting destroyer.

Maurice Wright was not the only one to undertake clandestine work on behalf of Captain Hall and Naval Intelligence. Leslie Harrison Lambert, one time magician and a Vice President of the Magic Circle, radio amateur, writer of short stories and BBC broadcaster, was a pivotal figure within the development of signals intelligence in his role as a 'radio expert'

Lambert was indeed a man of mystery. His obituary in *The Times* of 17 December 1941 revealed the death of Mr. Leslie Harrison Lambert who under the *nom de plume* of A J Alan had been a most popular BBC storyteller. Indeed those who have read *Most Secret War*, the wonderful book written by Professor R V Jones, will recall that upon his first visit to

**An early and also very rare photograph of Leslie Harrison Lambert. © BBC.**

Bletchley Park he had Lambert pointed out to him over breakfast and his secret identity revealed to him.

The obituary revealed that by the death of A J Alan at a Norwich nursing home on Saturday 13 December 1941 broadcasting had lost one of its most popular storytellers, and one, possibly the only one, who maintained his anonymity until the end. He was Leslie Harrison Lambert, a civil servant of Notting Hill, London, and around his personality and stories the BBC had created an air of mystery, which was at the express desire of Mr. Lambert. His quiet, clear diction, the interest of his stories, the delightful relief of the incredible anti-climax made A J Alan distinctive as an entertainer. He broadcast at most five times a year, the last occasion being on 21 March 1940. Mr Lambert was also an experienced amateur radio transmitter; and by reputation an authority on good eating and rare wines. Lambert had been one of the early amateur radio experimenters and held the callsign 2ST (later G2ST).

What The Times newspaper and everyone else did not realize was that from 1915, and perhaps earlier, Lambert had been directly engaged in secret signals intelligence work for the Admiralty and a part of the secret team working from Room 40. In 1919 Lambert had been one of the first recruits into the Government Code and Cypher School, secret work he continued right up to his death.

In 1977 Ronnie Wadman of BBC Talks recalled for Radio Four listeners how Lambert had been treated by young producers with all the respect due to a star performer. He described how Lambert would arrive for a broadcast dressed in a dinner jacket, with monocle and a briefcase from which he would remove sheets of cardboard, an India-rubber eraser, a steel tape measure, a stopwatch, a hip flask and a box of matches. His script was placed upon the cardboard so that it would not rustle. The steel tape measure was, having once been told that the perfect distance for his voice from the microphone was precisely eighteen inches, for him to measure that distance with parade ground precision. The India-rubber was to make any last minute alterations to his script and the stopwatch was so that he could time his delivery to the second. Recalling Lambert's rehearsal for the delivery of his short story *'Wottie'* in 1938, he was able to say that on each rehearsal Lambert ran for exactly the same time. It was then broadcast live on four occasions for domestic and external services, and on each occasion he ran for exactly nineteen minutes and twenty-three seconds – sheer perfection. The final item retrieved from his briefcase, the hip flask, contained fine brandy. Lambert was the only man known to be allowed to bring alcohol into the building!

In 1915 Lambert was to be found undertaking interception and direction finding work at a station located at Hunstanton in Norfolk. This proved to be the first of a network of interception stations set up by Commander R Bayntum Hippersley of the Royal Navy Reserve, another early radio amateur (callsign HLX and later G2CW). Hippersley, along with another amateur, Russell Clarke (callsign THX) had demonstrated to the Admiralty that, as experimental radio amateurs, they could receive signals to and from German warships at far greater distances than had been previously expected.

The equipment used at Hunstanton was installed by Captain H J Round and was indeed that which had been developed with Wright, including the recently developed direction finding equipment. Lambert, like Hippersley, was commissioned into the Royal Navy Reserve for the duration. However, there remains one mystery that has never been resolved, and that is how Lambert came to be at Hunstanton in the first place. Lambert had suddenly resigned from the magic circle in 1909 and vanished, so what had he been doing during that time?

Lt C T Hughes, the officer in charge of a DF station in Flanders.
© War Office, MoD 2014.

From the outset, Hippersley, Clarke and Lambert were able to intercept German naval signals which were taken down and sent directly to Room 40 at the Admiralty, where the codes were broken and the messages read.

There is one piece of light relief associated with the secret activity being undertaken at Hunstanton and this involved Queen Alexandra, who by this time was the Queen Mother. Her Majesty had embarked upon a coastal walk and had managed to avoid all of the naval guards that had been posted to deter inquisitive visitors to the site. Lambert had just taken over the radio watch when the person of the Queen appeared at the station. It was perhaps fortunate that Lambert had some time earlier appeared before Her Majesty at Marlborough House as a professional entertainer, and immediately identified the unexpected visitor. Accordingly all ended well. However, had the Queen been challenged by one of the unsuspecting armed naval ratings posted to guard the station, the outcome might have proved very different!

The Government Code and Cypher School (GC&CS) was established in 1919 within the Admiralty, under Commander Alistair Denniston RNVR. Its nominal purpose was that of advising as to the security of codes and cyphers used by all government departments and to assist in their provision. What was not disclosed was the requirement to study methods of cypher communications employed by foreign governments and their military and naval forces. From the very outset it was a most secret organization, being referred to as simply Room 14 of the Foreign Office to any individual or department that was not in the know, perhaps reminiscent of the Room 40 days.

At first, the 'school' employed some 25 staff who were drawn from the 'old hands' who had served so effectively within Room 40 at the Admiralty or Section MI1B of the War Office.

Buried within the *Edinburgh Gazette* of May 1920 the following appeared:

**Commander Alistair Denniston, RNVR.** © **Admiralty.**

*Under Clause 7 of Order in Council of 10 January 1910*

*Admiralty: Naval Intelligence Department:*
*Head of Coding Section – Alexander Guthrie Denniston*
*Senior Assistant (Deputy Head) – Edward Wilfred Travis*
*Senior Assistants – Oliver Strachey, James Turner*
*Junior Assistants – Robert Aitken, William Francis Clark,*
*John Hooper, George Leonard Nelson Hope, Robert Nigel*
*Carew Hunt, Alfred George Richard Rees.*
*Wireless Expert – Leslie Harrison Lambert.*

In 1922, it was arranged that the basic salary costs of this new but vital venture were to be met from the Foreign Office vote. In 1923 another element of the world of secrets was restructured with the Secret Service also being placed under Foreign Office control. The head of the Secret Service (always referred to as 'C') found himself with far wider responsibilities and in formal charge of the Government Code and Cypher School as its Director. Unfortunately, until World War II, GC&CS found itself very poorly placed in the bureaucratic pecking order. For the whole of the interwar period GC&CS remained a very small organization. By contrast, the total number of staff employed by GC&CS was recorded at 3293 as of December 1942 and reached a wartime peak of almost 9,000 by January 1945. It is perhaps interesting to note that the total Treasury estimate for GC&CS staffing costs for 1938 was £324,876 and that the salary allocated for Denniston as Head was £1,450.

Whilst the mysteries of codes and ciphers have always proved to be fascinating, this can easily lead to blinding one to the fact that this is just one aspect of a much wider and complex chain which leads from raw signals data to distributed intelligence report. Long before the cryptanalyst can set to work attacking a code; an interception of signals traffic must have taken place.

As an old recipe for rabbit stew once pointed out, before making your stew, first

# Fort Bridgewoods

catch your rabbit. The Government Code and Cypher School drew its rabbits from two main sources.

During World War I British censorship offices had been established at the various critical nodes in the international telegraph network, such as Hong Kong, Malta and Bermuda. In consequence, copies of all foreign government telegrams passing through these points, as well as those passing in and out of Great Britain, became automatically available to the British censorship authorities. Following World War I, and in accordance with reasonable peacetime arrangements, the process of censorship no longer had a place. However, Clause 4 of the amended Official Secrets Act of 1920, together with other appropriate arrangements, appear to have ensured that telegram scrutiny could continue on a fairly broad basis.

The second source of raw signals data was the Y-service, that is to say the interception of radio traffic by domestic and foreign stations operated by the Armed Services. The Royal Navy had established land based wireless interception stations at Scarborough and Flowerdown, and later operated a bureau for interception and cryptography in the Far East, initially at Hong Kong and subsequently relocated at Singapore upon the outbreak of World War II.

The War Office had first established a Military Wireless Interception Station at Chatham in 1921 under the control of MI1B, but this was placed on a more formal footing as of 09:00 hours on 21 March 1926, with the station located at Fort Bridgewoods being officially opened by one officer and five operators.

In those first days of operation the intercept operators, or Experimental Wireless Assistants (EWAs) as they were euphemistically known, had to provide their own illumination with candles during the hours of darkness. Their activities were

**Casemates at Fort Bridgewoods, that housed the first interception work in 1926. © Graham French.**

largely conducted underground, making use of the well-protected casemates and ammunition bunkers. Their first provided receiver was of French design and deemed completely useless other than for the reception of broadcast stations. Hardly an auspicious start to what would go on to prove to be one of the most highly effective wireless interception organisations!

In those early days of 1926 the staff kept office hours, working from 09:00 hours to 13:00 hours and following lunch from 13:00 hours to 17:00 hours Monday to Friday and then closed completely for the weekend. It was a far cry from the pace of life that was to follow for the Experimental Wireless Assistants in the years ahead.

1926 proved to be a year of turmoil and social unrest, and the country was soon in the grip of a General Strike. All of the staff at Fort Bridgewoods were former military wireless operators, so could send and receive the Morse code at high-speed and with great accuracy. Accordingly the Experimental Wireless Assistants were seconded to Chelsea Barracks in order to maintain wireless telegraphy communications between the seat of government in London and the provincial cities.

At the same time that the Fort Bridgewoods staff were being employed at Chelsea, Leslie Lambert was

Photograph taken around 1946, which includes Les Hadler, Jim Sparkes, Fred Hawkes, William 'Pop' Blundell and Sid Wort - the five Experimental Wireless Assistants who opened the Fort Bridgewoods station in 1926.
© *Beaumanor Staff Magazine*.

also preoccupied, but on a search for a clandestine radio station that had been identified by the Metropolitan Police radio station that was located at New Scotland Yard (Shaw House on the Thames Embankment). This had been established by Harold Kenworthy, another Marconi Company man and radio amateur (G6HX). Kenworthy had demonstrated some years earlier the value of radio communication and how it could prove invaluable in supporting day-to-day policing. The value of his work had been quickly seen and adopted, with vehicles being equipped with mobile radio equipment so that they could be quickly directed by the control station at New Scotland Yard. Kenworthy had been given the rank of Metropolitan Police Commander in recognition of the value his work. His operators were ex Royal Navy telegraphists who had been appointed as constables.

On the first day of the General Strike, 4 May 1926, one of the police operators on duty reported the reception of a very strong short wave transmission which was identified with the callsign AHA. Having consulted the relevant publication the operator had identified that this should identify a German station, although the Berne Lists of international radio callsigns showed that the current allocation of German calls had not passed AD-. From observation he had clear reason to believe that the transmission was far too strong to be coming from the continent, indeed it was so strong it had to be coming from somewhere not so very far away from his own station at New Scotland Yard.

Kenworthy, having by now had chance to hear the transmission for himself, immediately came to the conclusion that this was a clandestine station using a false callsign and this, coupled with the fact that it had come on the air just as the General Strike commenced, convinced him it was something sinister. In consequence he immediately contacted the Assistant Commission of Special Branch who in turn telephoned Admiral Sinclair, Chief of the Secret Service, and alerted him this worrying turn of events. Shortly after the alarm had been raised a Colonel Peel presented himself at the Police wireless station, accompanied by a dapper Leslie Harrison Lambert. Once convinced of the reliability of the police officers as communications personnel it was agreed that they would jointly attempt to locate the clandestine station, as it appeared likely that it belonged to a subversive organization directly linked to the General Strike. Use of the GPO, who at the time had a direct responsibility for all matters relating to wireless, was avoided as it was felt at the time that the Post Office employees were themselves on the verge of joining the General Strike.

Constables Wright and Smith, who both had service experience of direction-finding, were pressed into service, and the Marconi Company set to work installing two sets of improvised direction-finding equipment into Crossley Police Tenders. Clearly this was going to take some time, and with time of the essence Kenworthy made up a simple but effective direction finding set which he installed in a Gladstone bag.

The police operators continued to monitor the transmissions from station AHA and it soon became apparent that a network of stations was being established. Not intending to waste any time, Kenworthy and Lambert installed themselves into an otherwise empty plain van and whilst sitting on the floor in the cargo space as they combed the streets of London they became convinced that the clandestine transmitter was located somewhere in the area of Fleet Street.

**Crossley police tender, fitted for radio by the Marconi Company. © Metropolitan Police.**

The Crossley Police tenders, that had by now been fitted with the Marconi equipment, proved ineffective due to the received signals being reflected off the many buildings. Consequently it proved impossible to gain any realistic bearings that would permit any kind of triangulation of the clandestine stations location.

To achieve a better chance of tracking the station the Assistant Commissioner and the Secret Intelligence Service applied pressure so that access could be gained to the rooftops in the area surrounding Fleet Street. It did not take long for the pair to be able to close in to the rooftop of the building that contained the clandestine transmitter.

The raid by police proved to be a real anticlimax, as the transmissions were not from some nest of striking agitators but the very sober head office of none other than the *Daily Mail* who, believing that Post Office workers were about to join the strike, took what they believed to be all necessary steps to ensure they could 'scoop' the rival newspapers by having their own news reporting network. As it turned out the callsign AHA, which had first alerted the authorities, turned out to have been derived from the initials of the late founding owner, Alfred Harmsworth (Lord Northcliffe).

This successful collaboration did not go unnoticed however, at the time, it was hushed up.

As the General Strike came to its conclusion the five EWAs from Fort Bridgewoods were released from their emergency communications duties at Chelsea Barracks and

**Duplex transmitter and receiver built by L A Beale in 1921, whilst working for the Marconi Company, suggests one would be hard pressed to believe that anything he built would be anything other than professionally made.**
© Beale family archive.

returned to their interception duties.

Within days they were joined by their new commanding officer, Lieutenant Lionel Attwell Beale of the Regular Army Reserve of Officers, Royal Signals. His arrival brought new hope and their first real interception set, which he had built himself. Anecdotal evidence suggests that it was built in a tea chest, however, this has perhaps become mistaken over time with the telling. It is more likely to have arrived in a tea chest, to protect it from prying eyes.

From now on the station at Fort Bridgewoods was to keep a constant interception watch using this set, with the exception of weekends when the station was closed down at 23:30 hours on Saturdays and reopened at 09:00 hours on the Monday following. The initial task for the station was to monitor traffic between Paris and Beirut, with the intercepted material transported to London by special Post Office bag and delivered to a specialist cryptanalyst unit. This was followed by a further assignment involving a circuit from Tokyo, which linked to all of Europe's capitals.

In 1924 a Cryptography and Interception Committee had been established, upon which served representatives of CG&CS and the Armed Services. Meeting for the first time they attempted to apportion work and settle priorities in areas of common interest. Subsequently called the Wireless Telegraphy Interception Committee, it met only infrequently in the four years that followed. In 1928 this committee was substantially reorganised into a new body called the 'Y' committee under the chairmanship of Admiral Sinclair, and to which Leslie Lambert and Lt Beale belonged. The 'Y' committee was made up from members of the Admiralty, War Office and Foreign Office, and became the steering organization for all future interception work conducted by the Armed Services and Foreign Office. It should have driven all important work, but competing priorities and meagre budgets led to interception work being placed second to that of cable derived products and cryptography. This consequently led to the low morale that was to dog the staff of Fort Bridgewoods in the latter years of Lt Beale's command of the station. It was not his lack of ability as a leader or a wireless professional, just the general frustration at the lack of interest from those driving GC&CS, and the constant battle to fund the work at Fort Bridgewoods.

GC&CS had initially been entirely dependent upon the Armed Services for its radio interception. In principal, the attitude of the Armed Services was positive; after all there was no shortage of direct examples from World War I of how the golden eggs laid by code breakers had been supplied by interception geese. However, the armed services did not view GC&CS as an embryo intelligence service, but simply as a cryptological research bureau to which they could reasonably second suitably qualified personnel. In due course GC&CS established specialist departments: in 1934 a Naval Section, in 1930 a Military

## Fort Bridgewoods

Section and, as late as 1936, an Air Section. In real terms they had finally established a suitable internal framework for all kinds of signals intelligence collaboration. GC&CS became an inter-service facility, with all the cooperative gains that this implied. However, the Service departments remained reluctant to concede too much of what they regarded as their own spheres of competence. Traffic analysis, traditionally described as that branch of signals intelligence (SIGINT) dealing with the external characteristics of signal communications and, as such, a natural offshoot of interception, was an obvious case in point. However, there were to be many others. The British Army in India, as an example, maintained its own group of cryptanalysts who worked on traffic products which had been taken in the local theatre of operations.

This attitude continued to dog GC&CS and there lingered a view that it was mainly a peacetime store of competence which in wartime could be promptly and usefully dispersed and employed more efficiently in close proximity to operational headquarters. Perhaps more importantly to the way in which it had so far been developed, service intelligence directorates had no intention whatsoever of allowing the business of evaluating intelligence products to drift into the hands of civilians at GC&CS.

Indeed, achievements made by GC&CS during World War II should in no way hide what were significant deficiencies in its organization during the inter war years. Even allowing for the small size of its organization and the meagre budget allocated to it, it did indeed suffer from significant functional weaknesses and can be considered, in certain respects, as being a real victim of its own success. Josh Cooper, who joined GC&CS in 1925, was to recall that what was so striking about an organization which relied in the main upon wireless interception was that it showed a significant lack of interest in radio itself! For the 20 years between 1919 and 1939 most of the work carried out by GC&CS was on diplomatic products, with the vast majority of raw data coming from commercial telegraphic cable links. Indeed, wireless raw material was very much disliked by the cryptographers as it was largely, in their view, messy pencil script, not neat typescript and was often corrupt even when not obviously mutilated.

There is one further matter which needs to be cleared up at this stage, and that is why the GC&CS committee came to be known as the 'Y' committee. There have been many stabs at the reason for this, but the explanation is quite simple. It derives from Wireless Interception or WI for short. The letters W and I when sounded together sound quite simply as 'Y', and so the committee became named.

**Marconi five valve receiver.**
© **Marconi Company Ltd.**

Fort Bridgewoods, having established themselves as an effective interception organization within their first five years of operation, found their numbers increased with the addition of EWAs Felton and Kirkman joining in 1928, Abraham in 1930 and Bellingringer in 1931. There were to be no further additional staff employed until May of 1935, at which time the first commanding officer had suddenly died and a new commanding officer, Lt Cdr M J W Ellingworth RN Rtd was appointed. The station also gained a second receiver, similar to a Marconi five-valve set. With the new set came a new task – the interception of traffic transmitted from the Italian Legation in Peking.

Not all traffic was sent at a hand-speed that could be directly read by the EWAs of Fort Bridgewoods. A good deal of government and commercial messages were mechanically transmitted at very high-speed and, after 1928, Fort Bridgewoods was obliged to put in place equipment needed to intercept this material and permit its analysis. Lt Beale designed a new receiver and construction was started. However, due to the very limited nature of the funding arrangements for interception work, it took almost a year for it to be completed, with many of the components having to be hand crafted from second-hand materials. For example, it is known that the brass required for the capacitors was taken from the flash protection blinds that had been fitted into the fort's ammunition bunkers. Despite second-hand material being employed the quality of the build was of a high standard. Many hours were expended with hand tools at the bench in order to construct the mechanical components to the high standards expected by a Marconi man. Accordingly the final build worked well and it was brought into service. As part of this project the mechanical control of the interception was transferred almost immediately to London, where recording could take place. This permitted the product to be in the hands of the cryptographic centre within minutes, rather than having the delays introduced by post or courier services as was the case with other intercepted traffic handled by the station. Control of the receiver remained at Chatham, with an operator tasked to ensure that the receiver stayed on frequency, allowing for any 'drift' inherent in receivers from changes in temperature and unstable power supply arrangements.

Technically this was a very successful operation, with the audio output of the receivers being amplified and sent along dedicated telephone lines. The signal arriving in

London was passed into a mechanical receiving device, built by the Marconi Company and known as an undulator. This converted the audio signal into a pen trace on paper tape - long for a dash and short for a dot.

This arrangement between Chatham and GC&CS in London is no doubt the earliest example of remote reception and it proved very successful, so much so that it caused a demand from GC&CS for a second high-speed receiver to be built. This was completed and became operational at Fort Bridgewoods during 1930.

**A Marconi undulator of the type employed by staff at Fort Bridgewoods in their early work to intercept high-speed Morse traffic.**

# Fort Bridgewoods

By May 1931 the two high-speed interception operations were well established and due to the successes of the station so far there was clearly pressure at the Y Committee level for greater exploitation. Accordingly provision was made for ever more space to be found within the operational area. During the summer of 1931 the first high-speed transmissions from Tokyo were intercepted, the station using the call-sign JNA.

**The transmission masts of the Tokyo station JNA.**
© **Yosami Radio Station Archive.**

Observation of this station identified a link with Berlin, where hand-speed traffic was passed for about three hours every day. A good quantity of traffic was intercepted over this route and this grew exponentially in volume in a relatively short space of time whilst continuing to be intercepted by Fort Bridgewoods.

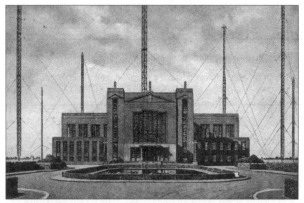

**Naeun (Berlin) radio station main building and some of the aerial masts, 1923. © Bundesarchiv.**

As well as the increasing traffic volume from this station, further Japanese transmitters were located and placed under observation. In the space of a few weeks it was established that almost all of the European capitals were in direct high-speed wireless telegraphy communication with the Japanese capital.

Around the time of these new observations by the EWAs of Fort Bridgewoods further technical advances were being made. New equipment was designed and installed to permit multi-channel working between the Fort Bridgewoods site and GC&CS in London, using just one GPO fixed landline.

Three channels were provided at frequencies of 4000, 7000 and 10,000 Hz. The first modern undulators were also provided by the Marconi Company, the UG6A.

For the very first time simultaneous remote interception of three high-speed wireless telegra-

**UG6A, which replaced the earlier Marconi undulator.**

phy circuits was available to the cryptographers of CG&CS in London.

The provision of this facility to intercept Japanese high-speed diplomatic traffic proved to be a very timely one, as the Japanese became involved in military operations in Manchuria which in turn significantly exercised the League of Nations. All three remote interception facilities were kept fully occupied during this period and many thousand Japanese Government messages were recorded for analysis by GC&CS, thanks to the technical innovations introduced by the commanding officer and staff at Fort Bridgewoods.

With the exception of two hand-speed routes that had been identified and put under early investigation, the interception and constant observation of Japanese high-speed traffic routes had become the primary priority. This should not be allowed to imply that there was no other work open to the EWAs of Fort Bridgewoods. There was indeed plenty of potential for interception work, but this was directly limited by the GC&CS priority with the Japanese target and the lack of financial resources within the GC&CS vote to permit further expansions in the provision of equipment necessary for interception work and, more importantly an expansion in the number of specialist operators who would be necessary to undertake greater observation and interception work. Until 1935 the establishment level at Fort Bridgewoods remained at one officer and nine EWAs. Whilst penny pinching remained the order of the day the potential for wider exploitation of an otherwise untapped intelligence source remained severely limited. Despite this there were in the wings plenty of well trained ex service wireless operators. Indeed the Commanding Officer of Fort Bridgewoods maintained a waiting list of some 50 highly trained ex service personnel who had previously been involved in interception activities in the field.

1933 and 1934 saw the staff at Fort Bridgewoods at a very low point, due to what appeared to be a clear lack of interest being shown in their work by the controlling authority. Lt Beale, their commanding officer, who had established a highly professional and effective team of wireless interception staff, had already identified the real potential for greater exploitation of this important source of intelligence, as well as introducing significant technical advances in the approach to harvesting the product. However, the highly efficient staff were starting to wonder if their work was felt to have any real importance to GC&CS and indeed if their station would continue to exist if CG&CS continued to focus upon the London end of the business, rather than investing in the front line work carried out at Fort Bridgewoods.

GC&CS appeared to have lost sight of the recipe for rabbit stew and was now trying to produce a nourishing meal without first catching their rabbits! Whilst the award of an MBE to Lt Beale in 1933 (*London Gazette* 21 December 1932) perhaps went a long way in recognizing the real importance placed upon their work to date, this uplift in spirits was to be totally wiped away when on 3 September 1934 the Fort Bridgewoods staff received the devastating news that their commanding officer had unexpectedly died at the age of 39.

**Lionel Attwell Beale's MBE and war medals.**

# Fort Bridgewoods

It is perhaps important to bring this chapter to a close with an incident that again involved Leslie Harrison Lambert and Harold Kenworthy which, in real terms, predicted the very future of 'Y' operations as it involved communist Russia which, at the close of World War II and the establishment of the Iron Curtain, was to become, along with the Warsaw Pact countries, the main target for the Government Communications Head Quarters (GCHQ) for the next 50 years.

In 1930 Lambert and Kenworthy were working closely together once again, but this time not against an enterprising newspaper owner but members of the communist party operating an illegal station on behalf of the Commintern. This fresh collaboration started with Kenworthy's operators intercepting traffic from a station with the callsign 8FD which was using amateur radio operator procedure signals and similar 'chatter'. The station was studied in careful detail and it was soon clear that it was being operated from somewhere close to Moscow and was controlling a worldwide network of stations, including one in the London area. Control of interception and direction-finding operations in this case was given to Lambert and Kenworthy who, by now, were both members of the 'Y' Committee, as was the officer commanding Fort Bridgewoods.

This proved to be the very first time that a foreign-controlled clandestine transmitting station was located in the United Kingdom and then kept under surveillance. So secret was this operations that it was to be many years before this incident was declassified and entered into the records held by the Public Records Office.

Two portable direction-finding sets in screened boxes with screened loops were designed and built by Kenworthy. This was indeed a significant technical advance at the time, which greatly improved the technique of short-wave direction-finding. The Secret Intelligence Service provided the unmarked van that the equipment and operators were to travel around London in. The travel arrangements, late at night as the clandestine station did not start transmitting until after 23:00 hours, posed the problem that the unmarked vehicle was likely to attract police attention and so the Metropolitan Police Commissioner issued a pass to the driver. The vehicle was indeed stopped, late at night in Thornton Heath, on one of its very first operational outings. As it turned out the pass issued to the driver by the Commissioner in effect only gave authority to drive through the Royal Parks. By luck no one checked the cargo area of the vehicle on this occasion, so Lambert, Kenworthy and the direction finding equipment remained undetected. This was not, however, the end of the episode, as later in the night they traveled to Kenworthy's home in Croydon and shortly after they arrived so did the same police officers who, rather than just take matters at face value, had spent the night following the van. Lambert and Kenworthy were questioned at length, but the officers were eventually satisfied with the explanation given by Kenworthy that he was the Wireless Engineer at Scotland Yard and he and Lambert were carrying out some very special experiments. It was perhaps fortunate that the police officers did not recognise the voice of one of their suspects as being that of the highly popular star BBC radio storyteller. Finding the elegant, fastidious, pernickety and almost 50-year-old A J Alan lodged on the floor of an unmarked van at the dead of night clutching some strange electronic gadget would have been the stuff of dreams for any tabloid editor and the story would have no doubt leaked to the press.

The illicit London station was finally tracked down to a house in Wimbledon. Special branch and SIS enquiries revealed that the house was occupied by a known communist,

working on behalf of the Comintern. A bold decision was taken by the authorities not to close down the transmitter, nor in any way alert the operator by any enquiry that might suggest that his station had been identified and was under surveillance.

The traffic being intercepted from the station was always in cipher and copies of the intercepts were brought to the attention of a senior cryptographer at the Government Code and Cypher School, Colonel John Tiltman. All the traffic was successfully broken.

The station remained in operation for a number of years, moving once to the home of another known communist in North London. As time went by the frequency of transmissions reduced, as did the quantity of coded traffic, and by 1937 it had virtually ceased altogether.

**Colonel John Tiltman, resplendent in tartan trousers.**

Kenworthy and Lambert remained important members of the Y sub-committee and indeed, in 1934 when the Officer in Charge of Fort Bridgewoods died suddenly, serious thought was given to Kenworthy as his successor. A second candidate was Captain F W Nicholls, who had previously commanded No.2 Wireless Company in Sarafand, but he promptly turned it down.

# Chapter 4.
# Another Marconi man

Lionel Attwell Beale was born on the 4 August 1895 at 61 Grosvenor Street, Mayfair to Gertrude Louisa Beale (nee Atwell) and Peyton Todd Bowman Beale, a consultant surgeon of Kings College Hospital.

The young Lionel Beale had been born into a well-to-do and prestigious family of doctors who had all reached significant status within their profession and were well published. Dr Beale and his wife also had two daughters; Margaret Gertrude and Phyllis Payton. There had been another child of the marriage who had been named Lionel Blakiston, but he was a sickly child from birth and had only survived until just beyond his ninth birthday.

Grosvenor Street, Mayfair, as seen in 2013. One can quickly establish the circumstances in which the Beale family were to be found in 1895.

Peyton Beale, his father, had been born in London on 20 June 1864, the son of Professor Lionel S Beale FRS, Professor of Medicine at Kings College Hospital, London. His grandfather was Dr Lionel John Beale and it is interesting to note that when it came time for the young Lionel to have his own family he named his own son Lionel John.

Peyton Beale had been educated at Westminster School and went on to study medicine, qualifying in 1888, shortly after which he was appointed as a house surgeon at Kings College Hospital.

His career and training progressed well and he was admitted as a Fellow of the Royal College of Surgeons in 1890. In 1893 he was appointed as an assistant surgeon at the hospital and full surgeon in 1901. He retired from Kings College Hospital in 1910 and was finally elected as a consulting surgeon in 1925, by which time he had his own cottage hospital in Hampshire. Whilst working at Kings College Hospital, Peyton Beale had been elected as lecturer in biology from 1891 until 1900 and demonstrator in physiology and histology from 1891 until 1904. For a number of years he was also lecturer in physiology and artistic anatomy in Kings College Hospital for women. He was also published, writing a book on elementary biology in 1894 and another, *Aids to Physiology*, in 1903.

From 1906 until his retirement from Kings College Hospital in 1910 he was Dean of the Faculty of Medicine. This was in the time when the medical school of the hospital was separate from the medical department and in consequence Beale had to carry out much of the administrative burden of his office himself. This situation continued until the two became joined and at this time he became the first Dean, when the new medical school came into existence in 1909. He was subsequently an examiner in physiology, and later in surgery, to the Society of Apothecaries of London, and further examined in surgery for Glasgow University and in biology for the London Conjoint Board.

Upon retiring from Kings College Hospital, Peyton Beal and his family left London for him to take up practice in Southampton, moving some ten years later to a house near Milford-on-Sea where he had a controlling interest in the local cottage hospital where he practiced as consulting surgeon. Along with his many medical interests Peyton Beale had a number of other interests, including being an accomplished botanist and microscopist. Strangely he was also very accomplished in wood and metal work and had an interest in all things mechanical.

Sadly Peyton Beale and his wife Gertrude were to survive their son by many years, Mrs Beale passing away in 1949 and Peyton Beale on Christmas Eve 1957 at the grand old age of ninety three. What is perhaps most sad is that when Peyton Beale died his obituary was written by friend and colleague J P J Jenkins, OBE, MRCS, who noted that the couple had two daughters, i.e. no mention at all of the two sons who had predeceased them.

As is fitting of the family of an eminent surgeon of the late Victorian era, the young Lionel Beale was sent off to public school, his father's choice being Uppingham School in Rutland. Most public schools of the day placed a strong bias upon sports and the Officer Training Corps, as well as the pursuit of academic achievements. Uppingham was no exception. Lionel Beale found himself in Farleigh House and from original documents held by the family it can be established that in 1913 he was representing the house in both the football and cricket first elevens.

**Uppingham School Rutland, around 1908. © Beale family archive.**

As has already been mentioned, the school had an Officer Cadet Corps and Lionel

# Fort Bridgewoods

was a member of this from the outset, gaining a proficiency in rifle drill and shooting.

Lionel was part of the shooting team and was reputed to be a good shot. Clearly this formative experience would have prepared him for service as an officer in the Great War, although nothing would have prepared him for the carnage he was to experience in the trenches. The school OTC uniform would have included a cap resplendent with badge which marked them out as Uppingham's.

Uppingham School OTC Rifle Company at Summer Camp. Inset is the Uppingham School OTC cap badge. © Beale family archive.

The school was founded in 1584 by Robert Johnson, Archdeacon of Leicester, who also founded the Oakham School where Marshall Ellingworth was completing his education around the same time as Lionel Beale was arriving at Uppingham. Old Boys include many famous names, but to pick out just a few; Rowan Atkinson, Donald Campbell, Sir Malcolm Campbell, Lt General Sir Brian Horrocks and John Suchet. Another well-known Old Boy is Stephen Fry. Sadly he was expelled from the school in 1972, although he does have his name immortalised in the fabric of his old school.

Uppingham School OTC shooting team. © Beale family archive.

Many of the old boys of Uppingham fought in the two World Wars, many giving their lives for King and Country. The School and the Cadet Corps are very proud of five of their number who won the Victoria Cross, the highest award for bravery in the face of the enemy; four awarded in the Great War of 1914-1918 and one in the Second World War 1939-45. One wonders if Rowan Atkinson and Stephen Fry had these old boys in mind as they filmed the final episode of Black Adder Goes Forth, as the whistle blows and they go 'over the top'.

Stephen Fry's name immortalised in the school's pavements.

Oral history within the family strongly suggests that Peyton Beale had set his heart on his son following him into the medical profession, although Lionel had expressed a strong wish to pursue a technical career in the fast- developing science of radio. Indeed, Lionel had clearly gained an interest in physics, and wireless in particular. By his seventeenth birthday he was doing something about this, as on 22 June 1912 Peyton Beale was issued with an amateur radio licence permitting the establishment of a wireless station at 'Oaklands', Hythe, Southampton. Whilst the licence was issued to his father there is a letter from the Post Master General that the licence, although for Lionel Atwell Beale, had to be held by the father as the son was still of minor age. It has been confirmed by the Radio Society of Great Britain that this was quite normal practice in the early years of amateur radio.

The oral family history is perhaps strengthened by an important document found amongst Lionel Beale's papers, following his death. A notice was issued by the University of London and further pages detail the full entry requirements for those young men who wish to volunteer as Junior Officers in the Regular Army. The year is of course most significant, being 1914, the start of the Great War. This document, along with the other pages can be found in the family archive alongside Lionel Beale's letter of application to be considered for a commission. Clearly Beale had been attending the University of London, although it is not clear what he was reading prior to setting aside his studies to go to war.

The University College London was closely linked to London teaching hospitals and it is documented that the University was lecturing on Physiology and that research laboratories had been established with monies gifted to them. There is no hard evidence from the Beale papers to confirm this theory, but there is certainly plenty of circumstantial evidence.

What is perhaps also interesting when considering this debate is that Beale in later lectures, given whilst working in India for the Marconi Company, mentions frequently the work of Professor John Ambrose Fleming who developed the two electrode vacuum tube and who was teaching at University College at the time that Beale would have gone up. No matter what the course of his academic career it is clear that, upon joining the University, Lionel Beale joined the University OTC and from here volunteered for Military service at the outbreak of war in 1914, like many others forsaking his academic career to serve his country.

**University College London Officer Training Corps . © *Illustrated London News*.**

The *London Gazette* of 31 March 1914 announced the commission of Lionel Attwell Beale as temporary Second Lieutenant. After his initial training he was appointed as a Second Lieutenant in the Hampshire Regiment, as of 1 September 1914. By 5 March 1915 he

# Fort Bridgewoods

had transferred to the Cyclist Corps and on 6 January 1917 he was transferred to the General List and attached to the Royal Engineers for Army Signals Service. Some six months later, on 1 July 1917 he was promoted to full Lieutenant, the rank he served in for the remainder of his wartime army service. His early war service was in Flanders and thereafter Gallipoli. Once appointed to wireless work with the Royal Engineers he served in Egypt, Salonica, Turkey and South Russia.

The Royal Engineers had some years earlier established the new science of wireless as one of the many strands to their Corps activities, because as yet the Royal Corps of Signals had not been established. At some point in 1917 Lt Beale, the signals officer, was selected as an Observation Officer and appointed to No.3 Wireless Observation Group deployed at Salonica. Wireless Observation was a service euphemism for wireless interception work.

Lieutenant Lionel Attwell Beale at the time of his commissioning in 1914. © Beale family archive.

Notes for the production of the Manual of Military Intelligence Chapter VI Section (3) – Technical and Intelligence Personnel and their Relative Functions - records as follows:

*2. OFFICERS. In addition to being experts in Wireless Theory and Practice, Officers for observation work must be first class operators and should know one or more foreign languages. On being selected for Observation Work they should be given some training in Cryptography.*

*5. Officers with Wireless Observation Groups should work in the Intelligence Branch as not only can the former frequently assist the latter in solving enemy cyphers etc, but information obtained from enemy intercepts will frequently be of assistance to the Wireless Observation Group (WOG) in identifying enemy stations. The more closely they work together, the more mutual assistance they can give to one another, and it would be well if selected intelligence officers were occasionally attached to W/T Units for instructions in the practical working of Wireless Telegraphy.*

During his time in Salonika Lt Beale clearly undertook significant work, as he was mentioned in dispatches. This was subsequently recorded in an announcement in the *London Gazette* of 5 January 1919. The following extract from a Memorandum by the Wireless Observation Organisation, British Head Quarters Salonika, 15 February 1917 gives some indication of the kind of interception work that was being undertaken by Lt Beale and his Wireless Observers:

| SECRET | Salonika 4<br>February 15th 1917. |
|---|---|

| Section 2. |
|---|

| Locations |
|---|

| 1(a) Military Stations |
|---|

| (1)  MACEDONIA | |
|---|---|

| DL<br>FF<br>AU<br>FY | The calls of the main stations at least have again been changed,<br>from the 10th inst. DL appears to have replaced SW at Uskub,<br>AU the former VY, and FY the former KX.<br>The routine practice of SW of FY exchanging calls with FF, VY and KX<br>at definite times every twelve hours is continued by DL with FF, AU,<br>and FY at the same hours.<br>The bearing of DL is that of SW, that of FY is that of KX;<br>but on AU the mean of 4 day bearings is 23 degrees while<br>that of VY was 20 degrees. |
|---|---|

| (i)  Eastern Front | |
|---|---|
| VY<br>FY | On the 9th one CHI and one ZIF - otherwise no traffic in the area |

| (ii)  Western Front | |
|---|---|
| | No calls heard. |

| (2)  OLD GREECE | |
|---|---|
| | No calls heard. |

| (3)  ROUMANIAN FRONT | |
|---|---|
| WP<br>MV<br>GK | Slight traffic between WP and MV and GK otherwise complete<br>inactivity. The Austrian stations have seldom worked. |

| (4)  RADIOGONOMETRIC stations and AIRCRAFT | |
|---|---|
| WOQ<br>WOR<br>WOX | were heard on the 10th sending + bearings timed 1334 to the<br>call GER (previously heard on 24/11/16) |
| GER | On WOR one bearing of 316.5 degrees (G) was recorded. At 1610 WOX sent balloon<br>soundings to a height of 4500 metres, prefixed 'CHIF HXWS' |

| (5)  OTHER ENEMY STATIONS. | |
|---|---|
| SM<br>SP<br>SY | These four stations, of whom the last three work with the Turkish naval group,<br>appear now to form a small group working in a code unlike that of any other<br>stations. (See Intercepts herewith) |
| SU | SM who has previously not been heard on a wavelength of less than A 300 degrees<br>has now been heard on A' 1200 calling SY |
| AY<br>YPZ | These stations are now heard daily, and day bearings have been obtained. AY has<br>a mean day bearing of 30.5 degrees (6 readings) while the night readings vary<br>from 30 to 65. YPZ gives mean of 320 degrees by day (4 readings) and is far more<br>consistent at night.<br>For AY one hearing from ZAB of 346 degrees gives an intersection at Bucharest, no<br>location is yet indicated for YPZ. Tuning up signals and ZIF's have passed but no<br>other communications: the communications of these two stations are peculiar to<br>themselves, intercepts are attached. It is worth noticing that certain isolated<br>words sent by them e.g. CASAR and BERTA are names of ciphers used by<br>Constantinople. |

# Fort Bridgewoods

Unrest in the Middle East had brought about a slowing down of demobilisation in the area and the Wireless Observation Groups were saved from being disbanded. Wireless Observation Group No.3, based on Salonika, was moved to Constantinople to carry out observation of Bolshevik traffic, following the Russian Revolution of 1917. They also kept observation on the traffic of the Turkish Nationalist movement in Asia Minor. The sister Observation Group, No.4, was moved to the west bank of the Tigris at Baghdad and kept watch on the Bolsheviks who were active in that area. These operations continued until as late as the end of 1923, when the War Office made the decision to evacuate all the British forces from Turkey.

By 1 May 1919 Lt Beale had returned home from Turkey, having been transferred back to the Hampshire Regiment. His service records show that as of that date he was appointed to the regiment in the rank of Lieutenant, with a seniority date of 1 July 1917. He was finally released from the Army on 1 January 1920, relinquishing his commission but retaining the rank of Lieutenant.

1920 was to find the recently demobilised Lt Beale working for the Marconi Company as a Wireless Engineer and he was clearly picked out to work on a prestigious project to develop what was to become the first commercial duplex wireless apparatus. On 11 May 1921 *The Times* reported a remarkable demonstration by Mr Beale of the Marconi Company, with two-way simultaneous wireless transmissions being made from Zandvoort in Holland to Southwold.

The Marconi Company archive, now held at Churchill College Cambridge, contains amongst its many files a journal kept by Marconi. From this one can establish some of the results gained from the Zandvoort to Southwold experiments. He notes remarkable differences in the behaviour of wireless signals in the 5 to 10MHz bands over different paths. At Southwold, some 175km from Zandvoort, the signal strength was noted to be much greater at night than during daytime. Despite the importance of these observations Marconi failed to recognize the use of the skywave element of the transmissions. It was to take him a further two years to rediscover what had been staring him in the face. Marconi seems to have had an affinity to huts during those early years, as is suggested by the photographic record of

The Marconi Company trials team at Zandvoort in Holland, 11 May 1921. Lionel Beale can be seen at the front centre of the photograph. The somewhat portly gentlemen wearing the horse blanket coat who is seen to the rear of the photograph is Mr Brain, who reported events for *The Times*.
© Beale family archive.

the day taken by *The Times*. Anecdotal evidence provided by the Beale family suggests that the *Times* reporter was so full of the experiment that he kept the point-to-point transmission running for over an hour, whilst he spoke with his editor. Meanwhile Beale and his team were concerned about the rising temperature in the power amplifier stage of the transmitter, which had not been designed for such an extended duty cycle. Perhaps a tribute to Beale and his team, the amplifier withstood this treatment and did not fail.

## Another Marconi man

Marconi was a very shrewd businessman and knew full well the importance of good publicity. Again, anecdotal evidence suggests that Beale did not take to Mr Brain, who he thought too pompous and full of his own self-importance.

From these experiments in Holland, Beale again found himself travelling and this time to India where he arrived in December 1923. Beale was based at the Marconi Company Headquarters which was situated at 5 Temple Chambers, Calcutta. Here he held the position of Head Technical Advisor on Broadcasting. As part of the Marconi technical staff he was also involved in the construction of one of the Marconi Company's long-range beam stations that linked the Empire by Wireless Telegraphy.

The buildings and aerial array of the Marconi Beam Station located at Kirkee, India. © Marconi Company Ltd.

During his time in Calcutta Beale set up a domestic broadcasting station based at the Marconi Company Headquarters which was operated under the callsign 5AF. Beale was responsible for the design and building of the 1kW transmitter, which provided good coverage of the order of two hundred miles radius. The station broadcast much in the same way as the London station 2LO, with regular music recitals, radio plays and talks. News was also an important aspect of the radio station and considerable press coverage was given to the station's ability to broadcast up-to-date news to this far-flung post of Empire.

The Marconi Company broadcasting station in Calcutta, call sign 5AF. © *The Statesman.*

During his time abroad Beale wrote a good number of letters of a domestic nature to his family, detailing daily life and giving some indication of the nature of the work he was undertaking on behalf of the Marconi Company. These were of course important and high value projects for Marconi, and the beam stations were designed to stretch the distances over which a regular and reliable traffic link could be established and thereby challenge the then monopoly of the cable companies. During his time in India Beale posed for the photograph which he sent to the family back in Hampshire. This photograph accompanied articles about his work which appeared in *The Statesman* and *Englishman* newspapers in February 1924. It is also perhaps interesting to note that in the same articles it was recorded that 2LO (London) had been received at a good signal strength on a number of days during the early part of 1924.

The family had, by this time, moved from Hythe, Southampton to Milford on Sea, on the opposite side of the New Forest, where Payton Beale was working as the consultant surgeon at the cottage hospital.

# Fort Bridgewoods

From the Marconi Company and India Lionel Atwell Beale reappears as the commanding officer of the newly opened Wireless Interception station at Fort Bridgewoods with five Experimental Wireless Assistants. All were well trained ex service operators of the recently formed Royal Signals, most having recently served in the Wireless Company at Sarafand. The station opened on 21 March 1926, but it took the Army some time to catch up with the formal appointment as his re-opened service record shows that he was appointed to a commission, in the Regular Army Reserve of Officers, Royal Signals in the rank of Lieutenant on 28 September 1926, with seniority from 1 June 1924. This latter date goes some way to support the station having been operating – in some form – since 1921, as indicated from the Denniston papers. It would perhaps have made some sense for trials to have been conducted at the Fort Bridgewoods site prior to the War Office nailing their colours firmly to the mast. It also, perhaps, goes to confirm the relationship between Marconi and the Secret Intelligence Service that is alluded to by Peter Wright in his book *Spycatcher*. He describes how technical solutions for the Secret Service (MI6) and MI5 problems, including funding, were often provided by Marconi through the 'old boy network' and indeed that Freemasonry played an important

This photograph accompanied an article in *The Statesman,* that detailed the work being conducted by Beale and the Marconi Company in India. It was taken by Bourne & Shepherd India, bespoke photographers well versed in producing posed photographs for English gentlemen and their memsahibs.
© Beale family archive.

part in that relationship. Lieutenant Lionel Atwell Beale was indeed a Freemason, belonging to the Pentangle Lodge which had its headquarters in Rochester. The Pentangle was predominantly a Military Lodge, set up to meet the needs of the local service personnel and retired officers. When it had originally been founded it met in the Sun Hotel in Chatham,

Members of the Medway Amateur Receiving and Transmitting Society (G5MW & G2FJA), holding their annual dinner in one of the fine function rooms of the Sun Hotel in the early 1930's. To the rear left of the photograph can be seen the roll of honour for the Lions Club. One of the supporters of the society was Captain L F Plugge, the Conservative Member of Parliament for Chatham and founder of Radio Normandie, the first commercial 'pirate' station that was so much a thorn in the side of Lord Reith, Chairman of the BBC.
© *Chatham Observer.*

a premises well used to supporting gentlemen's meetings in good surroundings and with fine dining.

By 1928 Lieutenant Beale was engaged to be married to Joan Hewitt, the 22-year-old daughter of a retired Royal Navy Captain of the engineering branch. It is perhaps interesting to note here that Miss Hewitt was living at that time at 8 South Avenue, Rochester, the very same road as Lt Cdr Ellingworth RN, was to move into during the late 1930's.

The 33-year-old Lieutenant Lionel Atwell Beal and the 22-year-old Joan Edith Hewitt were married in what would have been

Captain Lionel F Plugge MP posing with his radio fitted car, with the frame aerial prominent. The photograph was taken in 1931. He was a flamboyant character who had gained his commission in the Royal Flying Corps during the Great War, where he conducted wireless experiments. Captain Plugge presented the amateur radio society with a fine silver cup which is still awarded annually for outstanding service to the society.
© *Chatham Observer*.

a society wedding of the day at Rochester Cathedral. It is not surprising that they should have the wedding at such a prestigious location, given that the Cathedral is also the chapel of the Corps of Royal Engineers to which Beale had been appointed for his wireless work during the Great War. It was from this Corps that the Royal Signals, to which Beale was by now appointed, was formed.

The wedding of Lt Lionel Attwell Beale to Joan Edith Hewitt. The happy couple and family are posed at the West door of Rochester Cathedral in 1928. The best man, Peter Coles, is standing just behind Beale and to his right is Lionel's sister Phyllis. The lady on the left is the bride's elder sister Mary and the lady who is standing directly behind the bride is her mother Elleen Hewitt. It is believed that Captain Hewitt RN Rtd is the shadowy figure that can be just about seen in the shadow behind his daughter Mary.
© Beale family archive.

From the marriage certificate it can

Beale and his bride on honeymoon in Cornwall, as part of a motor touring holiday.
© Beale family archive.

# Fort Bridgewoods

be established that at the time of the wedding Lieutenant Beale was living at the Precinct Rochester, i.e. in one of the properties that surround the Cathedral Church itself and owned by the diocese.

By 1929 the Beale family was established in a very comfortable house at the upper end of the Maidstone Road in Chatham. The well-found detached property, named 'Coya', faced the entranceway to Fort Horsted and was only about ten minutes away from his Wireless Intercept station at Fort Bridgewoods, just a brisk walk along the path of the old narrow gauge railway that had linked each of the forts during the time of their construction.

'Coya' stood well back from the road and the entire area at the front was established into a rock garden, complete with ornamental fish pond. A pathway from a single gate, which can be seen on the left of the 1929 photograph, led to the back door which was always referred to by the family as the tradesman's entrance.

**'Coya', the Beale family home following the marriage in 1928. © Beale family archive.**

On the right hand side there was a wide driveway, leading to a garage for the car. To the rear of the house was a small lawn and flower garden, which led on to a tennis court and thereafter a large vegetable plot. John Beale recalled that as a child he seldom ventured into the garden at the rear of the house, because he was afraid of the gardener! Downstairs on the right hand side was the dining room, with the kitchen behind. To the left was the sitting room, to the rear of which was a conservatory which looked out onto the garden. On the upper floor left was the main bedroom and upper right John Beale's bedroom. John's sister, Anne Collette, had the room directly behind and this was shared with a succession of Swedish au-pairs.

To the rear of the garage is a large aerial mast with the long wire aerial trailing to a further mast visible above the trees at the far end of the garden. The status of the Beale amateur radio licence is unknown beyond its return in 1919 and may well have still been extant. He certainly maintained a workshop at the rear of the house, into which the aerial downlead disappeared. Neither of the children was allowed access to father's glory hole, but clearly wireless work was going on within the family home. No doubt this is the workshop where Lieutenant Beale built the Fort Bridgewoods interception receivers and where much of his experimentation for further advances that were to be made by Fort Bridgewoods was carried out.

Their first child, Anne Collette, had been born on 12 July 1929 and the second, named Lionel John after his paternal great grandfather, was born on 2 September 1931 at the Royal Navy Maternity Hospital in Gillingham.

'Coya' still stands on the Maidstone Road, but the front garden is no longer a place of rocks and the fishpond is long filled in. The bay window on the garage side at the front has been removed and replaced with one that is flush, and of course the young sapling is now a fully-grown tree. The aerial mast to the rear is long removed and some of the land in which Coya stood has been developed.

The *London Gazette* of 21 December 1932 announced the award of the Order of Membership of the British Empire (MBE), Military Division, to Lieutenant Lionel Atwell Beale, Regular Army Reserve, Royal Signals. As was discussed in the previous chapter, Beale's leadership and technical ability, along with the dedication and expert training of the EWAs, had forged the direction of wireless interception for the future and had established technical innovations that had revolutionised the work of GC&GS with re-

mote multi-channel line delivery of products directly to the cryptographers in London. The MBE was hard earned and well deserved, and it must have been a very proud day when Lt Beale and his wife attended Buckingham Palace for the investiture by King George V.

**The MBE, awarded to him by King George V at an investiture at Buckingham Palace in 1933, along with Beale's other war medals and sword, now take pride of place in the lounge of his granddaughter Heather's home in Cornwall.**

Sadly Lieutenant Lionel Atwell Beale was not to see his work bear the real fruits or have the knowledge that what he and his staff had worked hard to develop in those early years was to play such a vital part in events that would unfold in just a few years, and that would challenge the nation to its very limits during the dark days when Great Britain stood alone.

3 September 1934 started like any other lazy Sunday morning. Joan Beale had risen and was sitting at her dressing table, brushing her hair. Her husband was in bed. Whilst her back was turned on him she heard him making a strange noise and thought that he was fooling around, as he sometimes did. He did not respond to her mild rebuke and upon turning to face him she instantly realised that something was very seriously wrong.

Lieutenant Lionel Atwell Beale, Commanding Officer of one of the most secret locations in the British Empire and just 39 years old, was pronounced dead at St Bartholomew's Hospital Rochester that morning. Due to the sudden and unexpected nature of his passing a postmortem was required and the cause of death is recorded as follows: sub arachnoid haemorrhage of the brain, probably caused by spontaneous rupture of a congenital aneurysm. It was certified by Inspector S McLellan, Deputy Coroner for Rochester (without inquest).

Lionel Beale had been a time-bomb resting quietly for 39 years, capable of self destruction at any time. He had survived the rough and tumble of school games, the Officer Cadet Corps and the horrors of trench warfare only to die, without any cause or warning, in the comfort of his own bed.

## Fort Bridgewoods

The funeral of Lieutenant Lionel Atwell Beale, MBE, Regular Army Reserve, Royal Signals took place on 6 September 1934 at the Fort Pitt Military Cemetery which is situated on City Way in Rochester. The Service was conducted by the Reverend Henry Johnson, Rector of St John's, the parish church of Chatham.

Fort Pitt military cemetery dates back to a time when Florence Nightingale held great sway over the humane treatment of service personnel injured during the campaign in the Crimea.

Wounded servicemen from the Crimea campaign undergoing treatment at Fort Pitt Military Hospital, Chatham.
© *Illustrated London News.*

The first military teaching hospital was established at Fort Pitt and remained there for many years, until a new and larger hospital at Netley in Hampshire replaced it. The hospital at Netley eventually became a satellite of the Royal Navy Hospital at Haslar, Gosport.

Florence Nightingale had, through her introduction of nursing practice, revolutionised the treatment of battlefield casualties, which until that time had been utterly shameful. Her provision of clean and well-managed wards did much to reduce infection and relieve the suffering of the brave men who had been wounded, and in many cases suffered limb amputation, in the service of their country.

The funeral was attended by the whole staff of Fort Bridgewoods. Six, including William 'Pop' Blundell, acted as bearer party. A list of attendees was made by Mrs Beale, and this certainly makes interesting reading. The list establishes the esteem in which he was held by his staff at Fort Bridgewoods, his brother Freemasons from two

Note made at the time by Mrs Beale of those attending her husband's funeral. © Beale family archive.

lodges and perhaps, more importantly, those listed from the Foreign and War Offices. The first name jumps off the page; Leslie Harrison Lambert, who is styled as a colleague from the Foreign Office when in fact he was the 'wireless expert', fellow member of the 'Y' Committee and fellow radio amateur from the GC&CS. Captain McGregor from the War Office was in fact the Head of MI1B. Both were very much members of the shadowy world of the wider Secret Service.

During my search for Lionel Beale I finally tracked down his grave to Fort Pitt Cemetery, only to find it in a very sad state of repair. After a phone call to the Adjutant of the Royal School of Military Engineering at Brompton Barracks and a few minutes recounting that he had been commanding officer of Fort Bridgewoods, once one of the most secret locations in Great Britain, and a Member of the Order of the British Empire, I was soon able to convince him that something should be done. Sure to his word as an officer and a gentleman, within a few days the grave was as it should be.

The grave of Lt Lionel Attwell Beale MBE, Commanding Officer Fort Bridgewoods, 1926 to 1934, interred at Fort Pitt Military Cemetery, Rochester.
© Commonwealth War Graves Commission.

# Chapter 5.
# Out of the wilderness

World War I had proved a very costly business for Great Britain, both financially and in terms of the cost of human life. It was a reality that there was not a family in Great Britain that had not been touched by four years of brutal conflict.

By 1920 the cost of administrative government and our armed forces had risen exponentially. The 1913 Treasury estimate for maintaining the armed forces was £77 million, however, by the fiscal year of 1920/21 that estimate had risen to a staggering £190 million. It was not just the cost of the armed forces that was rising, the cost of administrating government itself was rising at a similarly alarming pace and the estimate for the Civil Service for 1920/21 was £590.7 million. Great Britain clearly could not stand these spiraling Treasury estimates and the taxpayer certainly could not and would not continue to bear them.

It is a very brave government that continues to raise taxes to maintain a large standing military force when you have just spent four long years fighting a bloody war that was believed would end all wars and settle the political direction of Europe in general for the foreseeable future. With a background of high unemployment and unrest about conditions for returning servicemen it was clear to Prime Minister David Lloyd George that he needed to take a lead if his government was going to maintain the confidence of the country and indeed that of the man in the street who, at the end of the day, decided their political future through the ballot box.

In 1921 Lord Rothermere, chairman of the Daily Mail, formed an Anti Waste League. Through the vehicle of his highly influential newspaper he applied mounting pressure upon the government of the day to reduce the burden of taxation and challenge them to take action against what was viewed as a wasteful Civil Service and an overgrown Armed Services.

David Lloyd George, Prime Minister of the day, did what all politicians throughout history have done; he formed a committee. In August 1921 he appointed Sir Eric Geddes to chair a committee which was to make recommendations to HM Treasury as to where the £113 million of economies, announced by the Prime Minister for the fiscal year 1921/22 were to be found.

Geddes had served in a number of significant government posts during World War I, first as Minister of Munitions, then as Inspector General of Transportation, followed by appointment as Controller of the Royal Navy in the rank of Vice Admiral and ending the war period as First Lord of the Admiralty.

Geddes took to his work with great zeal, with no element of the Civil Service or Armed Services exempted from the sharp cuts of his axe. Many career officers and other ranks found themselves beached or issued with bowler hats as a result of the fall of the Geddes Axe, and he was soon immortalized in cartoons of the day. The impact upon military spending was most significant and a continuing reduction in Treasury estimates, coupled with a general opinion that peace could be maintained without a need for a strong Royal Navy and large standing Army, meant that GC&CS were forever fighting a rearguard action to maintain their position within the food chain of government spending.

In the early 1930s times had remained hard, with continued penny-pinching and inter departmental fighting to gain the lion's share of what was available. Indeed, Geddes' promise to squeeze until it hurt was having a serious

**Sir Eric Geddes, author of the Geddes Act, responsible for the reduction in the armed services and public sector fiscal austerity during the interwar years.** © **Admiralty.**

**The Geddes Axe.** © *Punch*.

and detrimental impact on the vital work that was being conducted at Fort Bridgewoods. It was through these stringent times that Fort Bridgewoods had soldiered on, quietly developing new technical advances and firmly establishing that Wireless Interception was just as vital in the intelligence business as was the long-standing product access afforded by the cable companies. 1932 and 1933 had proved hard, with little attention being paid to Fort Bridgewoods by the cryptographers who ruled the roost at GC&CS and, as has been discussed earlier, preferred the typed script of cable product to the hand written script of hand-intercepted Morse code. But if the staff felt downtrodden, as 1933 came to a close they were in no way prepared for the disaster that was to beset them in 1934, with the sudden death of Lt Beale.

# Fort Bridgewoods

Whilst the government of the day and many in Great Britain paid little heed to the rise of an Austrian Corporal onto the stage of politics in Germany, this was not lost on the five old soldiers who worked as EWAs at Fort Bridgewoods. Despite the failure of GC&CS to appoint even a temporary commanding officer following the death of Lt Beale, they soldiered on until the close of 1934. Morale may have been low but there was a general determination to keep going and continue to provide the products and services demanded of them, even if GC&CS appeared to pay little heed to them being there.

In late December 1934 Lt Cdr Marshall John William Ellingworth, Royal Navy finished his final meal in the wardroom as a serving officer and quietly exchanged his impeccable uniform for plain clothes, paid his final mess bill and passed out of the gates of naval barracks for the last time. Ellingworth, a career naval officer and an expert in naval communications, had reached naval retirement age and was leaving the service for civilian life. It was the week prior to Christmas and he was secure in the knowledge that he already had new employment and his family would not want for anything as he moved ashore on a half-pay service pension.

There is no record of how Lt Cdr Ellingworth came to be offered the job at Fort Bridgewoods. It could be that he was already well known to Admiral Hall, indeed Ellingworth had recently been the Officer in Charge of the important Royal Navy Communications Centre at Malta, alongside which the service maintained an interception facility of its own.

Whilst one can speculate, what is without doubt is that with the arrival of the first week of 1935 Fort Bridgewoods welcomed its new commanding officer through its gates and a new spirit of optimism soon established itself amongst the staff. Ellingworth brought with him high standards and a need for a disciplined and organised workplace; all that one would rightly expect from a career naval officer. He was a professional wireless man and a very skilled operator when it came to Morse code and associated procedures. Lt Cdr Ellingworth was not always the easiest of individuals to work for and could be quite idiosyncratic, but his foibles could be forgiven when weighed against his professional capability and leadership skill.

Ellingworth was quick to acknowledge the importance of the work and the technical developments that had already been achieved by Lt Beale and his small staff, under difficult circumstances since they had opened the station in 1926. However, Ellingworth was determined that Fort Bridgewoods would expand and develop in order to meet what he saw to be the deteriorating world situation. His would be the most effective interception station, with the best trained operators producing the highest quality intelligence products. Ellingworth's determination was to prove vital if he was to convince the leadership of GC&CS of the importance of wireless interception and the intelligence products that could be delivered, given the resources that for so long had been denied to them. He would fight an uphill battle with the cryptographers to accept the hand-written scripts, but accept them they did, and when in 1940 the closure of Fort Bridgewoods was mooted it was to be the cryptographers who were first to jump to the station's defence.

By 1935 Europe was descending into political turmoil. Adolf Hitler and his Nazi party were in the ascendancy in Germany, with great showpiece annual rallies to demonstrate to the people and the world his domination of internal politics and his aspirations for the German nation to return to what he believed to be its rightful place upon the international stage.

The Versailles Treaty of July 1919 had removed land from Germany in order to provide a demilitarised buffer zone in the West, thus providing a perceived security for Belgium and France. Land had also been stripped from Germany in the East, isolating a large German community with the establishment of a corridor which gave Poland access to the sea port of Danzig. Czechoslovakia had also gained territory as a result of the treaty. The treaty required staggering financial reparation and the limiting of the size of the Ger-

**The German masses welcome Hitler to Nuremburg.** © *Volkische Beobacher*.

man Army and Navy, as well as imposing a total ban on the building of warplanes. The net result was that by the mid 1920s Germany was all but bankrupt and the international value of the German currency was at such a low level that the average German worker needed a wheelbarrow to take home his meagre week's wages.

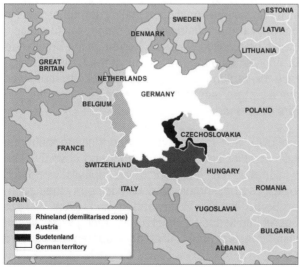

**Testing the waters and the resolve of The League of Nations, as Hitler retakes the Rhineland and expands into Austria and a swathe of Czechoslovakia.**

Whilst the world watched silently the little corporal tore up the Versailles Treaty and Germany was set on a new course to re-establish itself as the most dominant state within Europe. Hitler also had designs upon expansion, first taking back the lands lost under the Versailles Treaty and then by expansion to the east in order to provide what he styled 'living room' for the German people. Whilst Hitler ranted, the silent majority in Great Britain basked in the security of 'peace for our time', spurred on by a government whose policy was one of appeasement to ensure peace at any price.

## Fort Bridgewoods

There were but a small number of voices to urge caution and warn of the gathering storm clouds over Europe. Amongst these was one Winston Spencer Churchill MP, a dominant figure in the world of British politics, yet long removed from any position of political power or office of state. These were for Churchill what he subsequently described as his 'wilderness years'. Although out of office, Churchill warned the government of the menace of the extent of German military preparation and of the little corporal's expansionist intentions. He also maintained a vital briefing network, being kept up to speed with intelligence and technical developments by like-minded officers and civil servants in private and highly unofficial briefings.

When the Anschluss of 1938 saw Austria align itself fully with Germany what louder message could the little corporal have sent to show the world he was a serious threat to peace? Sadly those who should have been listening remained conveniently deaf. When his army marched across the border with Czechoslovakia the world did nothing. Poland proved to be the last straw and the British Government finally woke up to the gravity of the European political situation and

**Peace in our time, as the British Prime Minister returns from Munich. Not for long though.** © **Getty Images.**

offered guarantees to the Polish. The British Ambassador delivered a final note to Hitler, which he promptly ignored. Great Britain was once again at war with Germany.

But in the first week of January 1935 Great Britain was still at peace and there were other world affairs that were to occupy GC&CS and Fort Bridgewoods, long before they got down to the business of war with Germany.

Mussolini had taken power in Italy and had grand designs upon expanding Italian influence upon the world stage. He also had his eye firmly upon making territorial gains in the unsettled Middle East, where control over the oilfields was, perhaps, key to political power. The Middle East had continued to be a political powder keg since the British had redrawn the borders following the Great War. Had the mandarins of the British Foreign Office listened to Colonel T E Lawrence this region would have been a far different place and we would, perhaps, not have seen the many skirmishes and wars that have dogged it and the so-called First World Powers ever since.

Russia, the vast communist monolith, was taking every opportunity to influence world affairs by the infiltration of the capitalist states, both overtly and covertly. The Comintern was playing a vital role in infiltrating the very fabric of the capitalist world and this was the era of the recruitment of Stalin's Englishmen, who were to betray their country so thoroughly during the Cold War. Some, like Kim Philby and Anthony Blunt, were to hold important positions within the Secret Intelligence Service (MI6) during World War II and blithely pass secrets to their Russian masters about Allied developments which had otherwise been withheld from Stalin.

Spain was on the verge of civil war, with Germany and Italy supporting the fascist General Franco. Indeed the Germans practiced to good effect their Blitzkrieg tactics, in particular the deployment of the Stuka, for dive bombing both military and civilian targets. The addition of 'Jericho Trompete' (Jericho Trumpets) made it a true terror weapon. It was with all this in mind that Fort Bridgewoods rolled up its sleeves and went to work.

Ellingworth set about making small yet effective changes in the way in which the station was laid out and in improving the technical efficiency of operations. Two new locally made receivers were brought into service and the operators set about honing their intercept techniques. It was the laying down of these techniques and procedures that were to stand Fort Bridgewoods in good stead as war loomed in 1939.

During that first year of Ellingworth's command interest by GC&CS was rekindled and the station was given the task of conducting a detailed observation of Italian activity in Abyssinia. From the outset of October 1935, Italian military wireless stations had been detected by the EWAs at Fort Bridgewoods. Continued observation identified a full-scale network of stations in this theatre of Italian operation. By the close of the year Fort Bridgewoods had established the full extent of the Italian network, the point-to-point wire-less telegraphy link between Rome and the Italian command headquarters in Abyssinia, as well as all the subordinate wireless circuits. From this detailed observation the EWAs of Fort Bridgewoods were able to provide to GC&CS a high level of intercepted traffic for detailed examination.

1935 also saw the first tasking to carry out an initial examination of German military wireless communications, although this observation task was given a far lower priority that that of the Italian operation in Abyssinia.

The high-speed interception capability, pioneered by Beale, was put to far greater use with additional tasks to observe the League of Nations stations operating from Berne and Prangins, whilst the League was in session. There was also observation of transmissions from Italian Somaliland stations, Cairo and Shanghai, all of this in addition to the standing task of keeping under observation Japanese transmitters working into Europe.

A number of less important tasks were being carried out between executing the major tasks allotted to the station by GC&CS. In January there had been observation of tests carried out by an Italian station based in Rome, using radiotelephony to communicate with a station in Japan. The results were recorded as being of good signal strength with good speech quality received. During April a Russian station, believed to be OGPU - the State Secret Police - was placed under temporary observation. In May Fort Bridgewoods managed to identify seventeen stations using the Japan to Rio high-speed wireless telegraphy links. These were observed in the 4 and 6MHz bands. Observation was also conducted on Polish traffic, following the death of Marshal Pilsudski. In July sound recording tests were carried out whilst observing the Swiss station (HPB) located at Berne. These recording tests were carried out in conjunction with the BBC. The rounding-off of the year's minor tasks saw the station passing intercepted signals from Cairo by line to the GPO, with highly satisfactory results.

If 1934 had closed with the station at a low ebb, 1935 closed with rekindled spirits and a satisfaction that they were again doing real business and proving the value of the original GC&CS investment.

The year of 1936 opened with small sums of money being made available for the purchase of components, which permitted additional high-speed and hand-speed sets to be built locally. Whilst funding was still slow in coming, at least it was being pointed in their direction and could be used wisely to further advance the technical capability of the station. These additions allowed the operation of four high-speed sets and four hand-speed sets, but the limiting factor remained the staff establishment which by now had risen to nine EWAs. In July of 1936 GC&CS gave approval for the temporary employment of a further two EWAs.

The year's tasking was confined directly to the observation of the Italian war in Abyssinia and the high-speed services operated between Tokyo and the European capitals. Occasional observation was carried out of the stations at Berne and Prangins, as and when the League of Nations was in session.

**Italian military operations during the occupation of Ethiopia.**
**© Associated Press.**

The Italian occupation of Abyssinia had caused a consequent rapid expansion of the Italian military wireless telegraphy network and a far larger coverage became evident. The estimation provided by Fort Bridgewoods was that over 200 Italian transmitters were active at any time and that the meagre resources of the four manual receiving sets were placed under significant strain. Over 16,000 traffic items were taken from these circuits in December alone, of which 2,500 were enciphered.

Japanese high-speed traffic had remained at a stable level for the first half of 1936, but June saw a rapid expansion, rising to over 400% of its normal volume.

The Japanese observation required Fort Bridgewoods to deploy four high-speed receivers and normally two hand-speed, but often four, on a twenty-four hour basis, every day of the week. On many days up to nine Japanese high-speed stations were working simultaneously. Consequently there was no alternative other than to make a rapid transition from hand-speed to high-speed sets, to maximize the interception of Japanese government traffic. The overall volume of the observation tasks meant that only one EWA could be spared for the supervision of the four high-speed receiving sets. In consequence of the priority being afforded by GC&CS to these vital tasks, the observation of German military stations had been totally suspended for 1936.

The opening of 1937 saw the Fort Bridgewoods staff engaged in design and experimentation for the eventual production of a high-performance receiver, specifically engineered for interception work. This work and design ended with the introduction of the DST which, whilst a good technical receiver, was complex and demanded a highly competent operator to drive it to its full potential. Operators working with this receiver following its introduction to wartime service referred to it as a good receiver in the right hands, but most disliked it and much preferred the HRO, which was far easier to drive and demanded less attention from the operator. Plans were also drawn up to convert two casemates into set rooms, capable of housing six of the high-speed receivers and eighteen of the hand-speed sets. This was viewed as a somewhat ambitious project at the time.

Some movement was also seen on the staffing front, with GC&CS approving the employment of four additional EWAs as of January 1937. This took the total complement of operators up to fifteen. Clearly someone in GC&CS was finally appreciating the importance of the work being carried out by the dedicated team at Fort Bridgewoods, in spite of the continued restraint by HM Treasury and no real motivation on the part of the Government of the day to prepare for anything other than peace and appeasement. It appeared that the doors that were always firmly shut for Beale were finally being opened for Ellingworth.

The high-speed interception tasking for 1937 remained the observation and interception of Japanese traffic to Europe, and with the start of the Sino-Japanese war the traffic levels grew to over 400% of its previous capacity.

**Casemates at Fort Bridgewoods.**
**© Dr Philip Blenkinsop.**

Fort Bridgewoods was also tasked to a new hand-speed observation in the early weeks of January 1937. This was to provide coverage of all foreign military wireless activity from Spain, as a result of the start of the Spanish Civil War. This task was given a high priority and consequently all observation of Italian military operations in Abyssinia ceased from the end of January. From the outset the Spanish observation task revealed significant activity on the part of old friends of Fort Bridgewoods, the Italian military. The primary traffic circuits between Rome and Salamanca were soon under observation and a volume of traffic was intercepted. Also under observation were Italian circuits controlled from Salamanca and directed to stations under Italian control in important locations throughout Spain. The observation was so detailed that Fort Bridgewoods EWAs were able to identify and intercept mobile wireless telegraphy stations being operated by the Italian army units. Almost all of these mobile stations appeared to be operating on low power, which no doubt accounted for their traffic output being sent in plain language rather than in code. The Italian operators clearly did not appreciate the distance over which low-power transmissions could be radiated and in consequence intercepted. Despite their belief that this equipment would only radiate to a maximum distance of some thirty miles they were received at good signal strength over a full twenty-four hour period of each day at Fort Bridgewoods. Valuable intelligence about their activities was gained from the resulting interception.

For the whole of 1937 the EWAs of Fort Bridgewoods were so occupied with these primary tasks that any secondary attention to the German military target was shelved.

# Fort Bridgewoods

As the church bells rang out the dawn of 1938, Fort Bridgewoods was technically prepared for war. There were two set-rooms, one housing six high-speed equipments and the other eighteen hand-speed interception receivers. Approval in principal was also granted for a further expansion of the staff, complement by a further thirteen EWAs. These were taken on by June of that year. This brought the total staff up to 28. By September further expansion of the staff group was approved and another 48 EWAs were employed, bringing the total compliment to 73. With shift working, an allowance for leave and a small margin for sickness, this just about permitted the manning of the 24 sets currently installed at the station. The primary task of observing the Italian military operations in Spain continued apace and was placing ever-increasing demand on equipment time. It also allowed the EWAs to hone their interception skills, handling difficult groups under demanding and ever-changing reception conditions.

1938 had also seen the formation of a small traffic analysis section, staffed by Intelligence Corps officers. From the outset they were kept busy with the volume of traffic being intercepted. This experience was to prove highly valuable as the station moved slowly but inevitably towards war.

It was during 1938 that the EWAs gained their first experiences of signals security measures being taken by the Italian military operators, with daily changes of callsigns and regular frequency changes during each 24-hour period. This experience was to prove an invaluable one for the EWAs of Fort Bridgewoods, as the German operators were to prove far more adept with signals security measures than their Italian friends. It was further observed during this time that the Italians would impose radio silence before the start of any major operations. This was fortuitous in that that such orders for radio silence were always sent in a low-grade code which was simple to unpick at source and so prevented many hours of searching for alternate frequencies when radio silence was actually in force.

When there was any lull in the Italian wireless telegraphy activity the EWAs would be re-tasked to the German military target. This early observation gave Ellingworth his first indication of the scale of 'Y' operations that would be necessary to fully cover German communications activity if and when war arrived. It had been quickly observed that in excess of 26 German groups of stations were operating at the same time, many of these being ground-to-air stations. It soon became clear to Ellingworth that he had only a small fraction of the German military wireless telegraphy activity under observation.

From an interception point of view the German military operators proved to be highly skilled and efficient, and employed good signals security. Clearly the German military machine well understood the reality of interception by foreign powers and instilled good operating and security standards in their operators. Strict wireless telegraphy procedures were always observed, special 'Q' codes were used and there was no 'operator chat' that would offer any kind of intelligence to an intercept station. Daily callsign changes were in force, as was frequency changing, and all traffic was being sent in five-letter cipher groups. Fort Bridgewoods had indeed intercepted the first German Military Enigma traffic.

The Enigma machine was a complex encoding system that automatically scrambled, or encoded, messages typed into a keyboard by the operator. Whilst adopted and adapted for military use it had started life as a commercial system, designed at the end of the Great War by Arthur Scherbius, a German engineer. In 1923 he had set up his Chiffriermaschinen Aktiengesellschaft (Cipher Machine Corporation) on the outskirts of Berlin to manufacture and sell the device to the banks and railways for the sending of secret messages. The photograph shows an advert placed by the company from around 1924.

**Advert for the Enigma machine, circa 1924. © Cipher Machine Corporation.**

The military version relied for its security on the daily setting of three wheels, with electrical connections on their faces and a scramble of wires between the connections on each side. The number of permutations was increased by a daily choice of three rotors out of a total of five. There was a further increase in permutations by the use of an external plugboard (stecker board) at the front of the machine. According to Gordon Welchman, a vital member of the Bletchley Park cryptography team, the wheel-order, ring-setting and use of the stecker board gave 150 trillion possible settings for the machine.

The German high command believed absolutely that the system was unbreakable, but they had not been prepared for the Polish attack on the system in the run-up to 1939 and the work of GC&CS staff at Bletchley Park who had inherited all the work carried out by the Poles prior to their country being overrun. What was to also beset the German High Command and proved a vital gift for the British code-breakers was the frequent breaches of cryptosecurity, which placed the integrity of the Enigma cipher system at great risk.

1939 arrived and with it the speculation that war with Germany was imminent. The Government and many prominent figures of the establishment firmly believed in peace and the ability of the League of Nations to reign in German ambition and what appeared to the man in the street an inevitable road to war.

Fort Bridgewoods' task in the months leading up to the summer of 1939 was the recruitment of EWAs to place the complement of the station on a war-footing. During the command of Lt Beale the station had been starved of personnel due to the lack of interest shown in it by GC&CS and the penny-pinching attitude of HM Treasury. Beale had

**General Heinz Guderian, Panzer Leader, in his command vehicle during the Battle of France. This photograph demonstrates the number of personnel required to work with Enigma; one to operate the machine, one to read the output letters and one to send/receive the encoded message by Morse code. © Wehrmacht – Bundesarchiv.**

# Fort Bridgewoods

maintained a waiting list of about 50 highly competent ex services operators who could have been promptly employed should the financial resources have been secured by GC&CS for expansion, but this was not to be the case. In 1939, when approval for expansion was at last given, that waiting list was all but dry and it became instantly clear to Ellingworth that the recruitment of suitably competent personnel was going to be a significant problem once war was declared. The complement of EWAs did, however, manage to rise to a total of 75 by the close of 1939, and gave an operational capacity to man 20 interception sets. It was fortunate that under both Lt Beale and Lt Cdr Ellingworth the complement of EWAs had been established from well-seasoned service operators who were well versed in 'Y' operations. Ellingworth had also put in place a series of operational exercises which had further honed their skills, as had the valuable operational observation of Italian military activity during the campaigns in Abyssinia and Spain. This nucleus of professional intercept operators that now stood on a war-footing were more than capable of tackling nearly everything that was to be asked of them.

Post-war it was possible for Ellingworth, by studying captured German military documents, to compare the immediate pre-war modest standing of Fort Bridgewoods against that of the German interception organisation and there was a realisation just how small was the extent of the British effort at that time.

By 1939 the German military had established six large 'Y' stations. These were located at Konigsburg, Breslau, Treuenbritzen, Stutgart, Munster and Starnberg. They also had mobile stations that were capable of being deployed to specific taskings. In addition to the fixed stations, at least eighteen direction finding stations had been established, and when conducting foreign observations further direction finding sections were moved forward to locations which provided optimum opportunity for interception and direction finding. At least nine wireless interception companies were formed. Each company was established with three officers, 54 non-commissioned officers and 155 other ranks; a total establishment of 19,000 men.

The equipment deployed to each German fixed station in 1939 would have comprised:

Three long wave receivers – above 3000 metres.
Three medium wave receivers – 50-3000 metres
Three short wave receivers – 10-50 metres
Three ultra short wave receivers – below 10 metres
One long wave radio telephony set – above 200 metres
One short wave radio telephony set – 10-200 metres
Four high-speed undulators
Two Direction Finding sets – 350-4000 metres
Two Direction Finding sets – 120-450 metres
Two Direction Finding sets – 50-110 metres

Additional to all of these major items would be all the necessary amplification equipment and numerous ancillary items.

It was also established from interrogation of captured German documents that the

German interception organisation had allocated tasks to stations by country and that once that observation had been established it was maintained on a continuous basis. It was not permissible for observations to be curtailed, even if traffic levels reduced to a negligible level. It was clear that the Germans had taken their interception of enemy wireless stations very seriously indeed and when they had established breaches in operating procedures and signals security this intelligence was shared between their units to ensure such poor practice was avoided within their own organisation.

The interception of Japanese high-speed diplomatic traffic to Europe remained a Priority One task and additional high-speed observations were tasked as follows:

Rocky Point USA to Nauen in Germany
Rio de Janeiro to Tokyo and Europe
Buenos Aires to USA, London, Europe and Tokyo
Santiago to Rio de Janeiro and Tokyo
Shanghai to Japan and Europe
Chunking to Europe and USA

The six high-speed equipments operated at Fort Bridgewoods were fully occupied as the declaration of war moved ever closer, with intense levels of diplomatic traffic being intercepted.

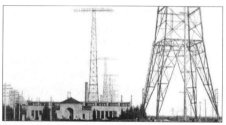

The American Medium and High Frequency radio station at Rocky Point. © RCA.

Stations such as Rocky Point and Nauen carried a multitude of traffic items of a commercial nature. The trick for the EWAs was to pick out the transmissions that were clearly encoded and in consequence would be the diplomatic gold-dust that GC&CS wanted to attack.

Aerial masts of the German station at Nauen, near Berlin. © Bundesarchiv.

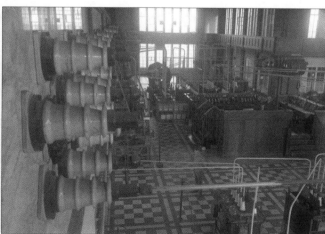

Internal view of the Nauen transmitter hall in 1932. © Bundesarchiv.

# Fort Bridgewoods

The observation of Italian military operations in Spain continued to occupy the EWAs during the first six months of 1939. All aspects of the Italian operation were being recorded, right up until the Italians made their entry into Madrid.

Shortly after this significant event in their military activities the entire General Head Quarters staff embarked upon the steamship Sardegna. Fort Bridgewoods continued to intercept traffic between the GHQ staff and the remaining Italian units located throughout Spain, right up until the ship finally docked in Naples on 5 June 1939.

Soon after this communications traffic levels went on the decline and consequently the task was reduced to partial observation, until it was finally directed that it should be abandoned during July of 1939. Up until the time of the Spanish Civil War all hand-intercepted traffic scripts were sent to GC&CS by registered post, causing an average delay of twelve hours. With the advent of the Civil War and the consequent increases in traffic volume it became increasingly obvious that such delays were no longer acceptable. By drawing attention to the high value of the intercepted

SS Sardegna as it leaves Spain for Naples, with its cargo of Italian Troops and the Italian General Staff. © *Esercito Italiano*.

material, the service members of the 'Y' Committee extracted an agreement to install a teleprinter link between Fort Bridgewoods and 54 Broadway, home of GC&CS and also MI6. Subsequently the teleprinter link was expanded to permit the sending of intercepts directly to Bletchley Park. Diplomatic traffic not covered by the high-speed observation task was also passed over the teleprinter link, to bring handling times down to the minimum possible.

Following Mussolini's unexpected occupation of Albania on Good Friday 1939 there was to be an addition of a further tasking relating to Italian military activity. As was their usual practice, the Italian command set up wireless communications and consequently observations were opened on wireless telegraphy links between Rome and Durazzo and Tirena, as well as other subordinate stations within the Albanian command area. The EWAs of Fort Bridgewoods had no difficulty at all in maintaining a constant observation and interception of traffic from the various Italian stations.

As the advent of war crept ever closer the observation of German wireless telegraphy activity became a Priority One task for the first time, with an ever-increasing number of sets being allocated to the task until almost all of the station's focus was upon the interception of German traffic. The high-speed traffic observations remained as previously tasked. The EWAs of Fort Bridgewoods settled to the observation of the German target, establishing in the first instance the certain identification of German operational groups and the composition and characteristics of their traffic. Initially, Fort Bridgewoods established two major German high frequency networks in operation and placed them under full observation. It was clear that their operating procedures and the characteristics of their traffic were almost identical. Both were sending traffic comprising five-letter groups of the type expected from the use of the Enigma cipher system. What could not be established from this observation was whether the stations were Military or German Air Force (GAF). The cryptographers of Bletchley Park were unable to provide any insight into this question as they were yet to break into these traffic streams.

The response from Bletchley Park was to ask Fort Bridgewoods to provide 500 intercepted messages every day, to support an in-depth analysis in the hope that this would lead to a break into the traffic stream. This demand caused some concerns for Ellingworth, as gaining 500 intercepts per day from these networks represented what would be a very heavy activity period for the Germans. In reality traffic levels were nothing like this on most days. It may be obtained from a time of crisis, but on almost every day his operators were making intercepts that would in reality prove useless, whilst other German activity went totally unobserved by the station as a result.

Greater understanding for the reason behind this request will be gained as the interplay between the cryptographers of Bletchley Park and the Interceptors at Fort Bridgewoods is looked at in more detail.

Fort Bridgewoods EWAs had some time earlier carried out observations on another significant German military wireless telegraphy network which was known to them as Wehrkreis. From close observation they had established that this network was run entirely upon the medium frequency waveband, with the control station being located in Berlin. This station controlled a main military grouping, including Wehrkreis Headquarters, which was roughly the size of a Corps area. The main group stations thereafter controlled groups within their own areas.

Shared intelligence made Ellingworth aware that the Wehrkreis medium frequency stations had been the subject of observation by the French military interception organisation for several years. The French were surprised and indeed skeptical when the Fort Bridgewoods observation suggested the existence of high frequency extensions to the medium frequency network. The matter was brought to a successful conclusion following a double watch set by Ellingworth, that is to say search and

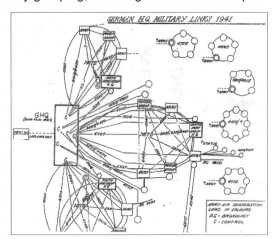

**Traffic analysis diagram of German military wireless circuits. 1941.**
© War Office , MoD 2014.

observation carried out on both medium and high frequencies simultaneously. It did not take long before the EWAs had intercepted identical messages which finally identified the onward relay of traffic initially passed on the medium frequency circuit and then extended outwards using high frequency circuits.

# Fort Bridgewoods

Having identified the main stations and their subordinate links this permitted an in depth observation over time and the outcomes were passed over to the Traffic Analysis section, recently formed at Fort Bridgewoods. This was a highly significant intelligence coup for the station and a full final report was made on the network and formations in March 1941. The chart gives some idea of the detail of intelligence that was developed by full observation, expert interception and the application of traffic analysis. The work car-

**Captain Owen (left) and Captain Jolowicz, intelligence officers at Fort Bridgewoods. © Howard Jellings.**

ried out in these early days at Fort Bridgewoods was to go on to set the standards for all future traffic analysis operations. Almost all of the process was still valid post war, as eyes turned to the activities of the Russian target. The establishment of the Compilation and Records Room (CRR) at Fort Bridgewoods was the first gentle step to the development of traffic analysis or SIGINT as it is better known today. This discipline was to develop significantly throughout the war period. SIGINT is, in short, the study of the 'who, when, what, why, where and how' of the radio traffic under observation.

Captain's Owen and Jolowicz were attached to Fort Bridgewoods as intelligence officers and were pivotal to the work undertaken to unravel the Wehrkreis network. Also significant to the analysis of signals was the collection and identification of callsigns, as well as operator ability, to identify individual German operators by the way they keyed their Morse code letters. Both enabled tracking of the enemy's moves as battle commenced, or their appearance at new locations suggesting a move of sections or regiments. Technical innovations such as radio fingerprinting were also pioneered by the intelligence team at Fort Bridgewoods, that is the taking of photographs of the individual nature of a trans-mitting set by observing its trace on an oscilloscope and noting any particular features that stand out when compared with other transmitters.

**H F Jolowicz, Professor of Law and by 1944 a Major in the Intelligence Corps. © Major Hugh Skillen.**

It is perhaps interesting to note the background of both Owen and Jolowicz. Prior to his volunteering for war service Owen was a school teacher, whilst H F Jolowicz, latterly a Major in the Intelligence Corps, was in civilian life a professor of law at Oxford University and had served as a Lieutenant in the Intelligence Corps during World War I. This perhaps reflects the importance of recruitment from universities, at the commencement of World War II which is discussed in some depth by Professor R V Jones in his wonderful account of intelligence matters *Most Secret War*. Hitler set great store by the pacifist views of many British academics and he was convinced that Great Britain would not go to war following the notorious Oxford debate where the motion was held that 'this house will not fight for King and Country'. When war finally broke out there was plenty of work for the academics, perhaps not directly on the front line, but in the development of weapons, in intelligence roles like R V Jones, and many found themselves at Bletchley Park breaking the German codes.

Dr Jones had one more passion which exercised his mind during his intelligence war and that was the issue of frequency measurement. Accurately calibrated radio receivers were still a thing of operator's dreams in the early days of World War II, and imprecise frequency measurements were to dog Jones as he attempted to unravel the German electronic beam navigation systems. Similar issues exercised Lt Cdr Ellingworth and he carried out some research which clearly demonstrated that our ability to accurately identify the working frequency of a particular station under observation was indeed flawed. From the table below it can be quickly seen what both Jones and Ellingworth were so concerned about.

Dr R V Jones, latter Professor of Natural Philosophy at Aberdeen University.
© R V Jones.

| Y Station | 13/07/1940 | 15/07/1940 |
|---|---|---|
| Bridgewoods | 5110 KHz | 6240 KHz |
| Harpenden | 5070 KHz | 6270 KHz |
| Cheadle | 5130 KHz | 6250 KHz |
| Chicksands | 5150 KHz | 6200 KHz |
| Sandridge | 5081 KHz | 6210 KHz |

The actual frequencies operated by this group and supplied later by the Germans was on 13/07/1940 – 5108kHz and on 15/07/1940 – 6237kHz. On each occasion only the operators at Fort Bridgewoods recorded the frequency within a very small margin of error. On 13/07 a margin of just 2kHz and on 15/07 a margin of 3kHz, on both occasions low of the actual frequency assigned.

The errors in frequency measurement were to prove particularly disastrous for the residents of Coventry, when British jamming proved totally ineffective against the German beam flyers despite Dr Jones predicting, quite correctly as it turned out, the beam frequencies to be jammed in advance of the raid. Why had the jamming not worked? It transpired that the frequency of the filters found in a captured German beam receiver had been measured incorrectly and the jamming note had been set to this observation as a result, and in consequence the filters rejected the jamming note and permitted the KG 100 pathfinders to correctly mark the target without hindrance. It is suggested that Jones stated that the person who conducted the measurements and made such a simple mistake should have been taken out immediately and shot. One could be sure that the residents of Coventry would have agreed with his sentiments, had they known of this disastrous mistake.

The frequency measuring instrument used at all British intercept facilities at the start of the war was one issued in around 1933 and could not provide anything like an accurate indication of the frequency in use. It was not until the introduction of the American receivers and the BC 221 that the EWAs could accurately measure and record working frequencies.

The discovery of the Wehrkreis network was a major coup for Fort Bridgewoods and fully justified all the training and hard work that had gone into everything they had done since they first opened for business in 1926.

# Fort Bridgewoods

The network of wireless telegraphy stations was clearly being utilised as an extension of the normal landline arrangements between Headquarters and Corps, and, what was more important, was that this proved to be the only pure German military activity capable of interception at that stage of the European war. It remained that way, with the exception of some low level formations, until a complete German Corps was identified as active in Libya in February 1941.

**The BC-221 frequency measuring set.**

This is very much what had been expected at the outset of the war as the meticulous Germans, known for their efficient signals security measures to deter interception activity, would not resort to wireless telegraphy communications all the time they had a highly efficient telephone network that could be thoroughly exploited. Without the enemy moving to wireless communications the chance of interception intelligence is nil and all the time the Germans were not stretching the traditional lines of communications they had no need to resort to wireless and the risks of interception that would always pose, despite the detailed security measures that were imposed for their protection.

As the Germans advanced into Belgium, France and Holland the amount of military wireless telegraphy waxed and then waned, as the traditional landline routes were established back to Berlin and subordinate headquarters.

This was certainly not the position when the Germans commenced operations overseas, or where a front was being established and fixed land communications were not established. In Russia and the Middle East the Germans relied totally upon extensive wireless telegraphy networks, all ripe for the picking.

Had the German army not extended beyond the Siegfried Line, the military 'Y' operation would have been a fairly small concern and the cryptographers would have suffered directly from a distinct lack of material for observation from interception sources.

The solving of a second German network that had been discovered during observation at Fort Bridgewoods proved a much harder nut to crack. By July 1939 a total of ten groups of stations had been identified and placed under longer-term observation. Through direction-finding this group of stations was identified as being located roughly in a triangle bounded by Dusseldorf, Kiel and Berlin, so covering most of the North West of Germany. Although they had been under observation throughout the whole of 1938 and now into 1939 the identity of these stations still had not been properly established. Whilst this area of Germany roughly fitted the command area of the 2nd Luftwaffen Gruppen Kommando, it did not include the southern area of the 6th Munster Luftgau, but did include the Western half of the 3rd Berlin Luftgau.

From the continued close observation that was being undertaken by Fort Bridgewoods it had been noted that during large-scale German air exercises between 28 July and 4 August, this whole network had enforced radio silence. As late August arrived there were clear indications that this network was being extended, with wireless telegraphy stations being established and becoming active on the Polish border. Fort Bridgewoods continued its observations and reported these important developments in intelligence. This expansion of the network was to prove vital in the process of eventual identification, as slips in operator procedure, operator 'chatter' and the use of Air Operating Signals (OPSIGS) strongly suggested that this was a German Air Force network.

It was this work that would fully justify the provision of a full Traffic Analysis section to work directly alongside the EWAs and this went on to be established as a very necessary part of the work at any 'Y' station.

There was one significant issue that continued to exercise the waking hours of the commanding officer, and that was what appeared to be a double objective. Why did the station exist, was it to provide proper wireless intelligence products or just the collection of cryptographic material. In reality the answer was clearly both at the same time, however, no one at GC&CS would make a clear decision on their relative importance. From the standpoint of the interception operators it was very clear that to date the cryptographic objective had been the ascendant one, strongly emphasised as the Enigma cipher could not be attacked until the wireless telegraphy intelligence objective had been properly achieved.

The identity of this network was not established by traditional interception and traffic analysis, but it finally became clear when Bletchley Park made its first break into the traffic on 6 January 1940. As had been strongly suspected from the slips in procedures made by the operators, this was indeed a German Air Force network and linked to the Luftgau, and using the German B book of callsigns.

# Chapter 6.
# Radio makes it possible

An earlier chapter has shown that the early equipment for wireless telegraphy interception was very much dependent upon the technical developments made by Captain H J Round and Maurice Wright of the Marconi Company.

The receiver relied upon a tuned circuit and a triode valve, which detected and amplified the incoming signals. The output from the valve was heard in a pair of headphones. This circuit, although used for secret work, had been published in amateur radio journals and was used by those radio experimenters who could either afford to buy a Round valve, or perhaps, as was commonplace with radio amateurs of the period, making their own using a car headlight bulb and foil on the outside to provide the control grid.

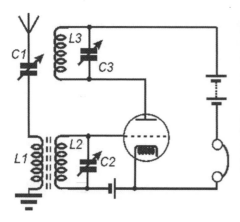

The earliest receivers would have relied upon technology developed by Captain Round and utilised his simple one valve circuit. © Marconi Company Ltd.

A reconstruction of the equipment used by Hippersley, Clarke and Lambert at Hunstanton, as they intercepted the wireless telegraphy traffic of the German Grand Fleet. © BBC.

Lt L A Beale, the first Commanding Officer of Fort Bridgewoods, was also a Marconi man and we have already seen the nature of his work in the experiments he conducted with duplex radio equipment in his attempts to provide two-way communications between Holland and England. One has to admit that, judging by the few photographs that exist to provide a physical record of his equipment, the work of the cabinet-maker was almost as important as that of the wireless engineer. However, there are great similarities with other Marconi receivers identified in this chapter and whose circuits were no doubt used by Beale as he produced bespoke interception receivers for Fort Bridgewoods.

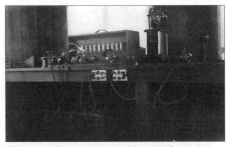

**Marconi Company early experiments with duplex radio telephone equipment. 1921. © Beale family archive.**

One would very much expect that the technical developments achieved by Beale, in particular in the early 1930's with receivers for high-speed wireless telegraphy interception, had behind them the cutting edge of technology being generated by the Marconi Company as we have already adduced that there was indeed a clear interplay between Marconi and the Intelligence Services. One would also expect that Beale, as a Marconi Man, would have been able to draw freely upon the research carried out by the Company, as well as using his own considerable competence in this important field of technology.

**Marconi 5 valve receiver. © Marconi Company Ltd.**

Wireless Telegraphy equipment available within the United Kingdom tended to run close to the developments of the Marconi Company and of course one cannot discount the many cutting edge technical developments which should rightly be attributed to the radio amateurs of this country. Military development in Great Britain did not keep pace with the commercial and military developments in the United States because we simply could not afford the staggering costs of research and development, given that the country was still suffering the fiscal impact of the Great War and the Great Depression of 1930. The military had been crippled by the Geddes Act and increasingly by the head-in-the-sand mentality of successive governments who could only believe in peace in Europe and chose not to see the storm clouds gathering as Hitler and Mussolini gathered both political and military power.

**Marconi 7 valve receiver. © Marconi Company Ltd.**

# Fort Bridgewoods

Prior to the outbreak of World War II commercial short wave receivers were not readily available in Great Britain and the EWAs continued to rely upon those that they designed and built themselves. A pre-war task for Fort Bridgewoods was the design of a modern wireless interception receiver and this eventually materialized as the DST-100, although it did not appear in operational use until 1941 and was, according to many operators, a difficult beast to drive when compared with the HRO, the first of the commercial receivers to cross the Atlantic.

**Marconi 226B receiver.**
© **Marconi Company Ltd.**

**R1155 receiver.**
© **Author's collection.**

Anecdotal evidence suggests that there was one company whose managing director was a short wave enthusiast and who as a sideline to his commercial enterprise produced a number of sets. Eric Cole, owner of E K Cole of Southend-on-Sea Ltd is believed to have been a close associate of Lt Cdr Ellingworth. Cole had one of his employees, George Hart, do modifications to the R1155 receiver for use at Fort Bridgewoods, prior to the arrival from the United States of the HRO, Hallicrafters radios and the RCA AR88.

**R1155 and T1154 outfit in the wireless operator's bay of a Lancaster bomber. Power for both transmitter and receiver was provided by rotary converters.**
© **Royal Air Force, MoD 2014.**

The R1155 receiver complemented the T1154 transmitter and the two were the standard Royal Air Force outfit for HF communications throughout World War II, including Bomber Command's long range heavy, the Lancaster.

The DST-100 was the product of a pre-war tasking for Fort Bridgewoods and had taken some three years from design to production stage. The DST or 'Diestys', perhaps a play on 'beasties', were not all together welcomed by the EWAs and many found them difficult to operate. Ellingworth described them as being a fine receiver in the hands of an expert operator. DST is believed to stand for David Scott Taggart, who was a friend of Lt Cdr Ellingworth.

The DST-100 was the first purpose-built receiver for British interception work and arrived in production at the time of the move of the main military 'Y' operation from Fort Bridgewoods to its temporary home at Chicksands Priory.

The DST-100s were operated alongside the National HRO receivers until they were, in the main, phased out in favour of the R206 and the RCA AR88. The receiver was designated for Army use, but was put to service in some Royal Navy shore 'Y' stations, alongside the navy's B28/CR-100 receivers. It was described as giving a high degree of intelligibility to weak signals. The modes of reception were CW [A1] and MCW [A2] and the frequency range was 50kHz to 30MHz continuously, in seven ranges. Blind spots were noted to occur in the region of the intermediate frequencies of 2MHz and 100kHz.

**DST-100 receiver, designed specifically for wireless interception work.**

Physically, the DST-100 was 15½" high, 24½" wide and 15½" in depth, with a weight of 110 pounds. The power supply was a separate unit and designated as Supply Unit Rectifier No.8. This had a height of 6½", a width of 7" and a depth of 13". It weighed 24 pounds.

The receiver provided for six different bandwidths. On the six higher frequencies, ranges A to F, the receiver operated as a double superheterodyne on the five narrow bandwidths; while on the broad bandwidth it operated as a single superheterodyne with an intermediate frequency of 2 MHz. On the lowest frequency, range G, the receiver operated as a single superheterodyne with an intermediate frequency of 110kHz and the broad bandwidth was not available. Variable regeneration was provided for the reception of weak signals. A Beat Frequency Oscillator (BFO) was provided for the reception of continuous wave signals (CW – mode A1). The DST-100 was mounted on two chassis, both housed in a single steel case.

The output of the receiver is terminated at 4,000 ohms for high resistance headphones. Provision was also made for a line output at 600 ohms.

The power supply for the receiver required a mains input of between 110 volts and

| Band | Frequency | Sensitivity (µV) |
|------|-----------|------------------|
| A | 30MHz - 12MHz | 2.0 (±0.5) |
| B | 12MHz - 4.8MHz | 2.0 (±0.5) |
| C | 4.8MHz - 1.9MHz | 2.0 (±0.5) |
| D | 1.9MHz - 0.78MHz | 1.0 (±0.5) |
| E | 780kHz - 310kHz | 1.0 (±0.5) |
| F | 310kHz - 126kHz | 1.5 (±0.5) |
| G | 126kHz - 50kHz | 2.5 (±0.5) |

**DST-100 CW sensitivity (for 20dB Signal to Noise).**

| Switch Position | Bandwidth for 6dB attenuation |
|-----------------|-------------------------------|
| Sharp | 1kHz |
| 2 | 1.4kHz |
| 3 | 1.6kHz |
| 4 | 1.8kHz |
| 5 | 2.0kHz |
| Broad | 12-25kHz |

**DST-100 receiver selectivity.**

# Fort Bridgewoods

250 volts in 10 volt steps. The frequency of the supply was 50Hz. The supply outputs to the receiver were 250 volts at 110 milliamps for HT, and 6.3 volts at 4.75 amps for the valve heater supply. The total power consumption was 95 watts.

The aerial system for the DST-100 was either an open wire or dipole with an impedance of 75 or 600 ohms, and the appropriate aerial coil input impedances were selected as indicated on an engraved plate that was attached to the rear of the receiver case. On the Mark 2 version of the DST-100, bands A and B were matched to 75 ohms only.

The first of the American receivers to arrive at Fort Bridgewoods was the National HRO. In 1942 an HRO cost $329.50 with four ham-band coil packs and the power supply cost a further $29.50. The general coverage coil packs, essential to the wireless interception stations, cost $18 each.

The National HRO was a valve-based short-wave radio receiver, manufactured by the National Radio Company of Malden, Massachusetts. Manufacture of this receiver commenced around 1935 and was aimed at both the military and amateur radio markets. It was to become the very popular mainstay of wireless interception work during World War II and remained in production in various forms until as late as the mid 1960's.

The National HRO receiver measured 48 x 22 x 33cm with a weight of 22kg. The case was steel and usually finished in a black crackle finish. At the top of the receiver was a lift up lid which afforded easy access to the thermionic valves, for prompt changes as they went soft with prolonged use. To reduce the level of hum generated within the receiver an external power supply was used. The other external accessory to the receiver was a separate loudspeaker.

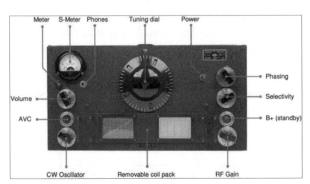

The National HRO receiver with controls annotated.
© Crypto Museum, Holland.

The HRO covered the entire shortwave band and was suitable for the reception of CW (A1), MCW (A2), AM (A3) and SSB (A3J) signals. All the controls for the receiver are situated on the front panel, with the two most apparent features being the precision tuning dial and the plug-in coil packs for the various bands. Bandspread coil packs were also available.

The Selectivity control at the right of the receiver is used when the single-signal crystal filter is selected. Setting the Selectivity control to the zero position turns off the crystal filter. The B+ control bottom right is used to turn the receiver off. When the receiver is used in conjunction with a transmitter, this control turns off the HT supply to the valves but leaves the heater supply intact, thus permitting almost instantaneous reception once the HT supply is reapplied. The CW Oscillator control is in fact the Beat Frequency Oscillator (BFO) which permits the reception of CW (A1) signals and the resolution of Single Sideband Voice (A3J).

The HRO receiver was normally supplied with a range of plug-in coil packs, one for each frequency band. These were normally stored in a wooden rack when not in use. Specifically for the amateur bands, coils A to D can be used which provide bandspread mode.

The development of the HRO receiver started in 1932, when the General Electric Company of America (GEC) was awarded a contract by the Bureau of Air Commerce to supply a short-wave transmitter and receiver

| Plug in Coil | Range | Bandspread |
|---|---|---|
| A | 14-30MHz | 10m |
| B | 7-14MHz | 20m |
| C | 3.5-7MHz | 40m |
| D | 1.7-4MHz | 80m |
| E | 900kHz-2MHz | |
| F | 580-920kHz | |
| G | 180-430kHz | |
| H | 100-200kHz | |
| J | 50-100kHz | |
| AA | 27.5-30MHz | |
| AB | 25-35MHz | |
| AC | 21-21.5MHz | |
| AD | 50-54MHz | |

**HRO coils packs and associated frequencies.**

unit for use in aircraft. At that time the company had no real experience in designing receivers, so they called upon James Millen of the National Radio Company to design a suitable receiver that met the required specifications of the contract. Millen produced a design that gave a superheterodyne receiver that covered 1.5 to 20MHz.

The original production models did not fully meet the requirements of the airlines and there was a requirement for better image rejection and selectivity. They also required a good Automatic Gain Control, which was not afforded by the original design.

James Millen undertook the new design at the National Radio Company, this time with the provision of two Radio Frequency amplifier stages and two Intermediate Frequency amplifiers at 455kHz, with a 20Hz crystal filter. The design was completed in 1934 and the National Company made a big push to have the receiver in production by the end of that year. This receiver was given the designation HRO, which anecdotal evidences was derived from 'Hell of a Rush Order', which indeed it had been to get the receiver into production in the timescale demanded.

Anecdotal evidence also suggests that in 1939 the National Company were told by the American military 'to start building HROs and we'll tell you when to stop'. It has been estimated that as many as 1,000 HROs were supplied as an initial batch to Great Britain,

| | |
|---|---|
| **Sensitivity** | 1µV input at 2 watts AF output into 7,000 ohms |
| **Bandwidth** | 4, 7.5, 14 and 21.5kHz |
| **CW Noise Equivalent** | 0.2µV |
| **Signal to Noise Ratio (at 5µV)** | -16dB |
| **Aerial input impedance** | 500 ohms (average) |
| **Maximum undistorted AF output** | 1.5 watts |
| **AGC** | flat within ± 10dB (between 10 and 100,000µV) |

**Technical specifications of the HRO receiver.**

with up to 10,000 following throughout the war years.

The Hallicrafters Company of America provided a number of excellent short wave communications receivers during the 1930/40s which found their way across the Atlantic and into 'Y' service. The Hallicafter SX-28A or 'Skyrider' came into use along side the National HRO and was from the same military and amateur radio stable. It retailed at around $223. The receiver seen here is in the standard 'Gothic' steel enclosure, but it was designed to be rack mounted so was more often seen without the enclosure. Like the HRO, the SX28A was supplied with an external speaker, many crafted with a lowercase 'h' logo, representing the first name of the manufacturers.

The SX28A 'Skyrider' proved to be a good general coverage communications receiver covering 0.54 MHz to 44MHz in six bands. Its design included variable sensitivity in three stages; sharp, narrow and broad IF. The receiver was provided with a Beat Frequency Oscillator (BFO) and a crystal filter for the reception of CW (A1). There was also a calibrated bandspread tuner and aerial trimmer. A signal strength meter was provided on the front panel to give a representative indication of signal strength.

**Hallicrafters SX28A 'Skyrider' receiver.**

The audio amplifier stage made use of two 6V6 output valves in push-pull configuration, which gave excellent audio quality. There was a bass boost function and a variable tone control. A headphone jack was provided on the front panel and to the rear of the set was provided two sets of speaker terminals, one at 500 ohms and the other at 5000 ohms.

As with most Hallicrafters receivers the SX28A power supply is provided internally, on the same chassis as the receiver.

The Hallicrafters S27 was classed as a UHF receiver and was special in that it was one of the first to use miniature Acorn valves in the front end. First designed in 1940, the S27 came in a steel cabinet in black crackle finish with dimensions of 19x9x14". Like the SX28A, it was normally rack mounted without its cabinet. The frequency coverage was 27.8 to 143MHz in three

| Valve | Type | Function |
|---|---|---|
| 1 | 6AB7 | 1st RF amplifier |
| 2 | 6SK7 | 2nd RF amplifier |
| 3 | 6SA7 | Mixer |
| 4 | 6SA7 | Oscillator |
| 5 | 6L7 | ANL / 1st IF filter |
| 6 | 6SK7 | 2nd IF Filter |
| 7 | 6B8 | Detector / S-meter amplifier |
| 8 | 6B8 | AGC amplifier |
| 9 | 6AB7 | ANL amplifier |
| 10 | 6H6 | ANL |
| 11 | 6J5 | BFO |
| 12 | 6SC7 | 1st audio amplifier |
| 13 | 6V6 | audio amplifier |
| 14 | 6V6 | audio amplifier |
| 15 | 5Z3 | Rectifier |

**Hallicrafters SX28A valves and usage.**

FREQUENCY MODULATION

AMPLITUDE MODULATION

145MC — 27MC (S-27)

THIS Frequency Modulation communications receiver covers 3 bands: 27 to 46mc; 45 to 81mc; 81 to 145mc. Switch changing from FM to AM reception. Acorn tubes in R.F. and converter system. High gain 1852 tubes in Iron Core I.F. stages. Beam power tubes in A.F. amplifier. Controls are: R.F. gain control. Band switch. Antenna trimmer. I.F. selectivity control and power switch. Volume control. Pitch control. Tone control. S-meter adjustment. AVC on-off switch. Send-receive switch. Phone jack. Amplitude or Frequency Modulation switch. 15 tubes. 110 volt 50-60 cycle AC. Dimensions: 19" long, 9" high, 14" deep. Model S-27. Complete with tubes. Shipping weight 75 lbs.     (FREMO)  **$175**00

| Band | Frequency |
|------|-----------|
| 1 | 27.8MHz-47MHz |
| 2 | 46MHz-82MHz |
| 3 | 82MHz-143MHz |

Above: Hallicrafters S27 band coverage.

Left: ARRL *QST* advertisement for the Hallicrafters S27 receiver. © ARRL.

bands. It had an Intermediate Frequency of 5250kHz and a Foster-Seely FM Discriminator circuit. The receiver was designed for the reception of AM (A3), FM (F3) and CW (A1). There was also provision for variable IF bandwidth.

The cost of a Hallicrafters S27 in 1940 was $175. They remained in production in the original format from 1940 until 1943, when it was superseded by the S27B. This receiver was one of the first to use Acorn miniature valves in the front end circuit.

The Hallicrafter S27 UHF receiver.

As with other Hallicrafters designs, the S27 had its own internal power supply on the same chassis as the receiver.

It was the S27 receiver that was flown in the reconnaissance Anson aircraft used to detect the German Knickebein beams that had been postulated by Dr R V Jones following breaks in Enigma Brown traffic intercepted at Fort Bridgewoods.

The Rolls Royce of the short wave wireless receivers that crossed the Atlantic in the 1940s was in no doubt the RCA AR88. Redvers Webber, an EWA at Beaumanor, was able to recall that at some time around 1942/43 he decided to provide himself with a good wire aerial for his own radio set and went to work to sling a suitable wire over the main house. In his aerial (in both senses of the word) antics, he arrived at the window of the office of his commanding officer, Lt Cdr Ellingworth, and was to get his first glimpse of the AR88 which was being evaluated by Ellingworth and Sid Wort. One cannot be sure who was more surprised!

The AR88 was a general coverage receiver produced by the RCA Company of America between 1941 and 1945, with large numbers be-

Acorn miniature electronic valves, as used in the front end circuit of the Hallicrafters S27 receiver. © RCA.

ing allocated to military use. Many were sent to Great Britain for wireless interception work and others were sent to Russia as part of the wider effort to support the Eastern Front, although little in the way of intelligence product flowed back as a result of their provision.

**The RCA Company AR88 receiver.**

The circuit uses two RF stages which make use of 6SG7 valves. The first detector used a 6SA7 and the oscillator circuit a 6J5. There were three IF stages using the 6SG7, a second detector and Automatic Gain Control used the 6H6, whilst the noise limiter a 6H6 and the BFO a 6J5. The audio frequency amplifier used a 6SJ7 with an output amplifier that used a 6V6GT. The power supply, like those of the Hallicrafters, was located on the main chassis and comprised a 5Y3GT rectifier and VR150 voltage regulator. All valves, with the exception of the audio output stage, rectifier and voltage regulator were of the metal type. The aerial terminals are located at the rear of the chassis and comprised of ports for 200 ohms balanced line or an unbalanced single lead in. The loudspeaker was again in a standalone enclosure and the output terminals for this were also located at the rear of the chassis.

The receiver was supplied in a black crackle finished steel case, with a top opening lid to allow easy access for valve replacement as they went soft with use. The AR88 was, like the SX28A, often found rack mounted, which is perhaps understandable given the weight of this equipment is around 100 pounds.

There were two distinct types of AR88, the AR88LF and the AR88D. The main difference between the two types is frequency coverage, but they also have different IF frequencies. The AR88D has an IF frequency of 455kHz and the AR88LF 735kHz.

| Band | AR88LF | AR88D |
|------|--------|-------|
| 1 | 73-205kHz | 535-1600kHz |
| 2 | 195-550kHz | 1.57-4.55MHz |
| 3 | 1.48-4.4MHz | 4.45-12.15MHz |
| 4 | 4.25-12.15MHz | 11.9-16.6MHz |
| 5 | 11.9-19.5MHz | 16.1-22.7MHz |
| 6 | 19.0-30.5MHz | 22.0-32.0MHz |

**AR88 types and frequency coverage.**

The receiver ran on power supplies between 115 and 240 volts AC, at between 25 and 60Hz, and drew around 100 watts.

The R206 receiver was designed by the British Signals Research and Design Establishment, although anecdotal evidence suggests that the hand of Sid Wort was also very much involved. Redvers Webber recalls it as the worst receiver he ever had the misfortune to operate in all his time at Beaumanor, as it had an alarming tendency to drift at the slightest vibration. The R206 came in two types, the R206 Mk1 and the R206 Mk2.

The R206 Mk2 was the big brother of the R107 and reputed by the Signals Research and Design Establishment as having impressive high performance. As can be seen by the comment of an EWA, the operators were not quite as impressed.

It was capable of mains supply operation from 100 to 240 volts AC or from a 12 volt DC supply, which gave it the ability to be operated in vehicles or in the field.

This was indeed the heav weight receiver of the wireless interception kit of the Second World War, weighing in at 120 pounds, with an extra 50 pounds for the power supply. The external dimensions of the receiver were 25x13x15", and it came with a box built into the protective framework which housed a multitude of spares, including valves and other sundry items.

**R206 Mk1 Receiver.**

The coverage of the R206 Mk2 was 0.55-30MHz in 6 wavebands and was designed to receive CW (A1) and AM (A3). Band changing was achieved by the movement of a large chrome plated handle which when turned into position pro-

**R206 Mk2 Receiver:**

vided a very satisfying clonk as it relocated the position of the turret tuner.

The receiver had a two-speed dial drive gearbox and vernier calibration. There was also provision of a calibrated oscillator control, to permit very small searches either side of the frequency assigned. It was perhaps the lack in stability of this circuit that may well have led to the frequency drifting complained of by Redvers Webber.

Selectivity was achieved in three settings; Narrow 0.7kHz, Medium 2.5kHz and Wide at 8.0kHz. Also provided was an AF filter. which was centred on 900Hz. Both the Narrow and the Medium selectivity settings had crystal filters.

The aerial input circuit incorporated a trimmer capacitor for matching and was designed for operation from 80 ohms coax. The valve lineup of the R206 Mk2 single conversion superheterodyne circuit was; the RF Amplifier using a ARP35, 2nd RF Amplifier using a ARP34, Frequency Changer using a ARTH2, Oscillator using a ARP35, both 1st and 2nd IF using a ARP34, Detector and 1st Audio Stages the AR21, Audio Output VT52, AGC amplifier the ARP34, AGC rectifier the 6H6 and the BFO using an ARP34.

The circuit of the power supply unit made use of two 6X5 rectifiers and was stabilized using an AW2. This valve was visible though a small window in the front panel of the power supply and loudspeaker enclosure, the glow providing assurance of operation of the power supply.

The one thing that is of vital importance in wireless interception work and which

# Fort Bridgewoods

often led to issues during World War II was frequency measurement, something that Dr R V Jones complained bitterly about on a number of occasions. Indeed during the post mortem of the Coventry raid he did indeed suggest that the person who carried out the frequency measurement of the audio tone being used with the German beam system should have been shot, as whoever he was he had made a very poor observation and measurement which led to the ineffective jamming despite having, by luck, identified the correct beam frequencies in use that night.

**BC-221 Heterodyne Frequency Meter.**

In the early part of the War frequency measurement was still being carried out using a device that had been in service since the very early 1930s and which had a very poor level of accuracy. This perhaps explains Ellingworth's observation of a single frequency on two separate days at various 'Y' stations, where the frequency measured differed by a considerable margin.

The introduction of the American BC-221 was a godsend and made the task of frequency measurement so much simpler. It was a heterodyne type frequency meter with an integral crystal calibrator and whose circuit made use of three electronic valves.

This equipment was used to set the frequencies of both transmitters and receivers over a broad frequency range of 125kHz to 20MHz.

On the low range the equipment operates between 125 and 250kHz using fundamentals. The high range covers 2 to 4MHz. The determination of all the other frequencies was achieved by using higher order harmonics of fundamental frequencies.

The operating manual provides an indication of the maximum error that can be expected when measuring a frequency of 4MHz at an ambient temperature of minus 30°C, and this is given as being in the order of 1.355kHz or 0.034%. In practice only perhaps half of this error would be observed. Under the favourable conditions found in most 'Y' station locations far greater accuracy would have been gained from this device.

The fold-down lid contained a book of tables that cross-referenced the dial settings observed to actual frequency and, whilst far more cumbersome than today's frequency counters with direct digital readout, this equipment was to provide valuable service at Fort Bridgewoods and beyond.

# Chapter 7.
# Fort Bridgewoods goes to war

All intelligence activity needs to be coordinated and managed. The work of Fort Bridgewoods came under the coordination of GC&CS, through the 'Y' Committee, and was tasked with specific pieces of work that were then graded by priority.

As of 1939 the War Tasking for Fort Bridgewoods was communicated as follows:

*To intercept all traffic between enemy allied GHQ, and between those HQ and their respective Governments.*
*To assist field units in interception of traffic between enemy General Headquarters and lower formations.*
*To intercept all high-speed enemy military traffic other than the above.*
*In War the Army will not be required to undertake any interception of diplomatic high-speed traffic.*

This was the theoretical role of Fort Bridgewoods as directed by GC&CS, but in practice it was to prove to be very different. With the exception of the Wehrkreis observation (and even this was suspended for long periods in 1940 and 1941) together with the observation and interception of ground formations during the occupation of Norway, Denmark, Holland, Belgium and France, Fort Bridgewoods found itself focused almost totally upon the interception of German Air Force signals.

Whilst clearly the observation and interception of German Air Force traffic was at odds with the primary directive given to Fort Bridgewoods, one can understand why the interception of air traffic was so important. Clearly at this point in time Bletchley Park needed volume of product in order to carry out its own cryptographic interrogation and Fort Bridgewoods was providing high quality intercepts of what was currently one of the only wireless telegraphy sources that was consistently using the high-grade Enigma cipher.

# Fort Bridgewoods

The Royal Air Force arm of the 'Y' service was not to start the interception of high-grade Enigma traffic before 1941, no doubt because during 1939 and 1940 there remained much confusion within the higher command chain as to the actual origin of the signals coming from Germany and the occupied territories. Until Bletchley Park finally made a break into the traffic there was no certainty as to its origin, despite Fort Bridgewoods' traffic analysis already reporting indications of Air procedures in use, Air-related operating signals being used and, perhaps more telling, operator 'chatter' which indicated a link to the German Air Force. Consequently the task of observation and interception was left with Fort Bridgewoods, which had discovered the source in the first place. This was perhaps fortuitous, given the developments of 1940 when the German Air Force commenced wide scale attacks in the skies over the Home Counties, which was to become known as the Battle of Britain. The German air assault was designed to give them air superiority and precede the invasion of England. This culminated in the wholesale bombing of London and the era of the Blitz.

Despite detailed searches by the EWAs of Fort Bridgewoods, little further German traffic was identified and in consequence they were free to maintain an unhindered observation of this vital intelligence strand.

During the Battle of Britain Lee Mallory and Douglas Bader, advocates of the 'big wing' tactic, were highly critical of the conduct of the air battle by Air Marshall Dowding, the Head of Fighter Command. The Air Marshall was directing the battle in a manner that he believed minimized the overall demand upon his precious pilots and aircraft, whilst still delivering consistent and effective violence to the enemy. What only a handful of people were aware of, and Dowding could not reveal his secret, was his access to the very thoughts of the German High Command, thanks to the breaks made by Bletchley Park into the air traffic that was being intercepted by Fort Bridgewoods. It was not until the late 1970s, with the publications of books finally revealing the Ultra Secret, that the tactics employed by Dowding were at last understood and vindicated.

**Air Chief Marshall Dowding, the Head of Fighter Command during the Battle of Britain.**
**© Royal Air Force, MoD 2014.**

As 1940 arrived Fort Bridgewoods had settled well into its war-time role. The war-time staffing establishment had at last been set and approved at 132, all of which were to be civilian EWAs. With this number in mind the commanding officer was faced with the task of recruiting, a formidable task when there had already been a call-up of all reservists and the imposition of conscription into the armed forces. His task was made all the more difficult when some of his own existing older and experienced EWAs were recalled to their own services.

Ellingworth employed a number of methods to meet the operational establishment of the station, including setting up a small training school through which suitable candidates could be trained to read Morse code and inducted into the mysteries of wireless interception.

Andrew Connolly joined the Royal Navy in 1933 as a boy and was trained as a wireless telegraphist. Much of his time was spent working in shore stations, although he did have drafts to sea. In 1937/38 he was stationed in the Admiralty's wireless telegraphy station at Aden, returning to Great Britain in the latter part of 1938 to join HMS Pembroke, the Royal Naval Barracks at Chatham. He was married in the summer of 1939, as war was fast looming over the horizon. From his Royal Navy record of service can be established that on 20 March 1940, having been graded as being below the standard of fitness for continued service with the Royal Navy, he was discharged. Following two weeks terminal leave he joined the 'Y' Service and took up his appointment as an

**Sub Lieutenant Andrew Connolly RNVR.**
**© Connolly family archive.**

EWA at Fort Bridgewoods, where he still retained his rank as a Sub Lieutenant with the Royal Naval Reserve. He was to remain with the 'Y' Service until November of 1946, when his service time with the Royal Navy came to an end. As the country was six months into a war it does not seem likely that the Royal Navy would have given him up lightly, indeed the service retained arrangements where personnel with reduced fitness could be retained on suitable shore duties and just not employed at sea. One comes to believe that Ellingworth had pulled a few strings with friends in high places to arrange for Connolly, a highly trained naval communicator with a high level of competence in Morse code, to be transferred to 'Y' work and fill just one of the gaps in the Fort Bridgewoods establishment at such an important time operationally.

Some further indication of likely string pulling can be assumed from the fact that after completing his service with the Royal Naval Reserve and in consequence the 'Y' Service, Connolly went on to have a second career as a school teacher and specialised in physical training!

Another insight into recruitment to Fort Bridgewoods in 1939 was given to me by Dr Philip Blenkinsop, whose father and uncles worked at various times for the 'Y' Service. Mr Reg White, Dr Blenkinsop's uncle, joined the staff of Fort Bridgewoods in early 1940 and was given a fairly lowly position as a messenger, taking intercepted traffic from the set-room to the intelligence staff and teleprinter room. When bombs started to fall during the Blitz, Lt Cdr Ellingworth took pity on him and told him he should not risk his life by crossing the open parade ground area. Instead he was given permission to take the short-cut through the commanding officer's personal office. Six months later, when the bombing had long since ceased, the short-cut so generously offered by his new found friend was still being exploited, until one day Ellingworth could stand it no more and requested that he kindly revert to using the normal thoroughfares to conduct his business in the future.

# Fort Bridgewoods

Former Sergeant Jean Robins of the ATS has given a description of her service at Fort Bridgewoods as a teleprinter operator in a BBC project to record the oral history of World War II. Robins, service number W/768, joined the station in 1938 and recalled that there were aerial masts in the middle of the camp and men in rooms who took down the Morse code, later the famous Enigma code. The civilian operators took down the German signals that they were intercepting in handwritten script and then passed it by messenger to the teleprinter room, where ATS girls like Robins sent it on to No.4 Intelligence School, later Bletchley Park. The ATS girls seen sitting in the photograph were some of the originals employed at Fort Bridgewoods in 1939. The ATS girls worked shifts the same as the civilian EWAs and as the work intensified they also did night duty. Most of the intercepted traffic was in five letter code groups, which was really boring for the ladies in the teleprinter room, although this was often enlivened by Japanese diplomatic traffic which had been transmitted in plain language. Robins and the other ATS girls were barracked at Brompton, in a block behind the officer's mess, and transported by lorry each day to the Fort. She also recalled that many of the other girls who worked at the station at this time had been locally

ATS teleprinter operators photographed at Chicksands Priory. Those sitting and kneeling in the front row had been previously employed at Fort Bridgewoods.
© Joan Nicholls.

recruited from the Sharps Toffee factory in nearby Maidstone. Sergeant Robins remained at the station until the move to Chicksands in early 1941. She recalled the evacuation of the Fort Bridgewoods site was as a direct result of the invasion scare.

The Sharps Toffee factory in Maidstone, Kent where women drafted to work at Fort Bridgewoods had been previously employed.
© Sharps Toffee Company Ltd.

Whilst the Compilation and Records Room was established with an injection of six officers from the reserves, the recruitment of those who would perform the routine tasks was a little more difficult. It was finally resolved by placing a carefully worded advert in the local papers. There was a volume of replies to this, which gave little away about the nature of the work to be performed. From the candidates a number with appropriate qualifications were recruited into the secret world of Fort Bridgewoods.

Len Moore, who the author had the privilege of interviewing a couple of years before he passed away, had been posted to Fort Bridgewoods as a recently trained operator with the Royal Corps of Signals. Len recalled his arrival at the station and that it was a secluded place that was bordered on the eastern side the Rochester-Maidstone Road. The only entrance was approached along a track way in a wooded area, which led to the bridge which spanned the deep moat. The main entrance was guarded and had heavy metal doors. Len also recalled that as you passed through the main entrance doors you entered a passageway which, after a short walk, divided into two. These passageways then led to the two parade squares. As you exited the right-hand passage you came back out into the open and there was a building made from wiggly tin sheet, and beyond that were the casemates. Len also recalled that where the entrance corridor divided towards the two parade squares, in the gloom one came across a very strange sight; a large, full body figurehead from an old sailing ship.

Ellingworth, being a retired Royal Navy officer, was determined to assert a naval influence on his command and had somehow managed to acquire a figurehead from one of the old wooden walls of the Royal Navy. It has not been established how Ellingworth came to be in possession of it, but one can surmise that it was on loan from the Dockyard at Chatham which had a fine collection, as did the Dockyard at Sheerness. The figurehead was reputed to depict Admiral Cornwallis and this was certainly how Ellingworth had it painted, with a blue coat. There is strong speculation that the figurehead was actually of General Cornwallis, who had lost America for King George. There is certainly a Kent connection to Cornwallis, as a wooden wall of that name ended its days as a floating jetty at Sheerness Dockyard and two local Sea Cadet Units have gavels made from timber which

**Cornwallis ship's figurehead, which stood in the entrance tunnel at Fort Bridgewoods and post 1941 in the courtyard at Beaumanor.**
**© Ken Carling.**

was recovered from the ship when attempts were being made to clear the jetty by the Sheerness Docks Authority in 1957.

HMS Cornwallis, an 1,808 ton, three-deck, 74 gun 'wooden wall', was launched on 24 February 1815. Built in Bombay for the Royal Navy, it was constructed of teak as

**HMS Wellesley, built in Bombay and sister ship to the 1815 HMS Cornwallis.**
**© Royal Navy, MoD 2014.**

opposed to the usual home construction using oak. The vessel perhaps played its best-known role when, as a flagship at Hong Kong, it was used for the signing of the Treaty of Nanjing which brought to a conclusion the Opium Wars. HMS Cornwallis was, in later service, fitted with steam engines, but, as was the fashion of the day, retained its standing rigging and sails. The ship was subsequently brought to Sheerness where as a hulk it was transformed into a floating pontoon.

HMS Wellesley was a sister ship of the 1815 Cornwallis. Both were built in the Dockyard at Bombay for the Royal Navy and from a bill issued for the carving of the figurehead it is suggested that the one for Cornwallis was very similar

# Fort Bridgewoods

to that of Wellesley. The figurehead from HMS Wellesley has for many years greeted anyone who passes into Chatham Dockyard through the main gate and is not a full torso. Ellingworth's figurehead does indeed have legs, which is unusual in a Royal Navy figurehead – although by no means unknown.

HMS Cornwallis of 1815 is no doubt not the best fit for having provided the Figurehead, despite the local connection. There were previous ships of a similar name and one, the Marquis of Cornwallis, was in 1800 used to transport convicts to Australia.

Joan Nicholls, who wrote the wonderful book *England Needs You*, the story of the ATS Special Operators who carried out 'Y' work at Beaumanor, has spent many years trying to establish the true identity of the figurehead and one hopes that one day she will break this particular Enigma.

Anecdotal evidence suggests that after the EWAs left Fort Bridgewoods for Chicksands the figurehead was stored in a barn somewhere in the vicinity of the Fort. Nashenden Farm is nearby as would have been, at that time, the farm buildings associated with the Borstal institution which was under the control of the Royal Navy. One suspects that nomatter what the true story was it would have involved yet another of Lt Cdr Ellingworth's personal

**The Figurehead from HMS Wellesley that stands just inside the main gate at Chatham Dockyard.**

contacts. When the station at Beaumanor was finally opened the figurehead found its way into the main house courtyard and stood there until 1953, when Ellingworth finally retired from the 'Y' Service. Brigadier Duvivier, who took command of Beaumanor after Ellingworth, did not appreciate having a naval figurehead in his military station, so had one of his supervisors quietly dispose of it. The job went to Harry Dix, who gave it to a good home – Loughborough Sea Cadets. One suspects that somewhere in an archive there is a personal loan record that shows that Ellingworth signed for a figurehead and as yet he has failed to return a valuable item of naval stores!

**Members of the Fort Bridgewoods Home Guard, taken in 1940 by Howard Jellings. It shows the EWAs, Ellingworth, his deputy Sid Wort (who is the only one in civilian attire) and the two Intelligence officers. Clearly seen in the foreground are two Lewis machine guns. One assumes that these would have been used to provide a murderous hail of crossfire from the angled fighting chambers that were set into either side of the main entrance-way to the Fort.**
**© Howard Jellings.**

All of the EWAs, although carrying out vital war work, were classified as civilians. In consequence they were required to belong to an organisation helping the war effort – Fire Watchers, Air Raid Wardens and of course the Home Guard. The staff of Fort Bridgewoods formed their own Home Guard unit, with their only real task to provide security for their own station. Standing guard on the windy earthworks of the fort with a Lee Enfield rifle and one round of ammunition proved to be a very lonely task, particularly during the height of the Blitz. At the end of the duty the rifle would be unloaded of its one bullet and the weapon and ammunition returned to stores.

Chris Barnes, who trained as an EWA at Fort Bridgewoods, recalled having to stand all-night fire duties as a member of the Home Guard. From the earth ramparts one was able to see to the North Fort Borstal, which was fully manned by the Royal Navy. Fort Bridgewoods was a quiet and lonely place at night, with the duty watch of EWAs secure and hard at their interception task in their deep bunkers and the Thames Estuary in the distance. Barnes recalled being stood alone on many nights watching German bombers tracing their journey across the darkened sky on the way to London, using the river to mark their way. For a young man like Barnes it was a memorable experience.

Whilst Ellingworth was expanding the station to meet the war role he was still very much focused upon the needs of the code breakers at Bletchley Park. Although on the list of those who knew of the work being carried out at Bletchley, his staff were not. However, there was a general assumption amongst the EWAs that code-breaking was going on and that was the reason for the demand for such a high volume of intercepted traffic in five letter groups. Whilst Bletchley were concerned about anyone getting a hint of what they were doing they need not have worried about Fort Bridgewoods because, although the EWAs had their suspicions, they were not about to speak about it, much in the same way they would never reveal to anyone the nature of the work they were conducting. Whilst from the very outset in 1926 there had been established a necessary framework of operational security, Ellingworth had ensured that it was absolute.

Another important aspect of work during the first year of the war was the fitting-out of the deep underground rooms which were to be used during the air raids that were expected, because of the close proximity of the Royal Naval Dockyard at Chatham and the airfield at Rochester, whose north-western edge was just some 500 yards away from the Fort. Rochester airfield was one of the many auxiliary Royal Air Force stations. It was also home to Short Brothers, who manufactured the Short Sterling bombers. Short Brothers were a well established aircraft company, mainly associated with flying boats, with their main factory located a few miles away from Fort Bridgewoods on Rochester esplanade, close to the Norman castle. Shorts were well-respected and had provided the flying boats for the Empire Flying Boat Service. They had also produced the experimental piggy-back plane, where a large flying boat carried a smaller one clamped to the top of the wing and which could then be released in flight to give a large increase in range for the delivery of overseas mail. Also located on the northern edge of the airfield was Pobjoy Engineering, who manufactured all-important aircraft components and engines. The Pobjoy site is now occupied by BAE Systems, formerly Marconi, who very much remain in the aero industry.

The idea of the deep operating positions was to ensure that the interception tasks could continue in the face of enemy bombing that would pose a significant risk to the

# Fort Bridgewoods

existing upper casemates, despite the thick concrete and earth banking. It was vital that the primary task was not interrupted and consequently a deep set-room was established over 90ft below ground level, although it did not see too much action as the station was evacuated to Chicksands not long after completion. Despite the often intense bombing, operations at Fort Bridgewoods were only interrupted once and this was for a four hour period due to the main power supply feed cable being severed when a bomb exploded in a nearby field.

Even with the threat of invasion and the intense bombing activity of the German Air Force, morale at Fort Bridgewoods remained high and cases of absenteeism were extremely low, despite the dangerous journey to work for the EWAs, in particular for those presenting themselves for the night watches. Many of the operators had to make journeys of up to five miles to get from their homes or billets to the comparative safety of duty in the underground set rooms.

**The counterscarp gallery built behind the walls of the moat at Fort Bridgewoods. The access tunnel below the moat provided an area of deep shelter. © Graham French.**

It was during this intense period of activity that one of the EWAs, Eric Millhouse, who was affectionately known as 'Mouse', started to write and circulate the *Chronicles of St Upid* (STUPID) which was to tell the story of the EAWs or 'tribe' as they undertook their work and, like the tribe of Israel before them, wandered in the wilderness. Millhouse wrote his chronicle in the manner of the Old Testament, with Abraham replaced by a new leader OSEE (OC) who EWA Wilkinson 'Wilk' drew with an uncanny likeness to Lt Cdr Ellingworth. Ellingworth, who we will see from a later chapter, was a very religious man, but took this in very good part. To show his support for this work, Lt Cdr Ellingworth wrote a short introduction and appended his signature below.

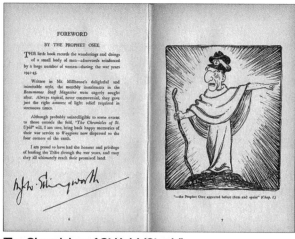

**The Chronicles of St Upid (Stupid).**
**© Connolly family archive.**

During 1940 the primary task for Fort Bridgewoods remained the observation and interception of German Air Force traffic, which provided a high volume of messages encrypted in the Enigma high-grade system. There was, however, partial observation carried out of Russian wireless telegraphy activity from Finland during the early months of that year.

With the intense air activity which accompanied the German invasions of Norway, Denmark, Holland, Belgium and France, and subsequently the Battle of Britain, came extremely high volumes of wireless telegraphy traffic transmitted in high-grade Enigma. During this period there were fluctuating changes in the demands made on the interception regime, to meet the tactical situation. Whilst German military operators from earlier observations had proved to be efficient and security conscious, it was not to prove the case with the German Air Force once the war had started. Operator 'chatter', slips in signals security and, more importantly, poor cryptosecurity was to prove the very weakness that was needed by Bletchley Park if they were going to make any progress in their attack upon the Enigma machine code.

As well as the primary work above there were a number of special tasks allocated to Fort Bridgewoods. Towards the end of 1939 a large network of high-frequency wireless telegraphy stations was observed by the EWAs. This remained an important task until the end of 1940. The network was identified as 'Luftgau' and over the wireless telegraphy links were passed a high number of short messages, known as short reports, which detailed the daily serviceability of German airfields. This work was highly important as it provided detailed information about the German Air Force order of battle – and this very much informed the tactical thinking of Air Marshal Dowding as he commanded the Battle of Britain. It was also this traffic which later in 1940 gave an indication of the change in tactics and the relief from heavy daily attacks on London and the Home Counties. The work on this network was significant and the intelligence officers at Fort Bridgewoods were able to produce a grid map pinpointing all of the German airfields and their formation identity. This particular network covered the whole of Germany, parts of Austria and parts of Czechoslovakia. The large network was broken down into groups known as Funkbereich, or wireless areas, and each was allocated particular working frequencies. Each station within the wireless area would make its short report daily to the Area Control Station, who in turn reported this to the next higher authority. Whilst all this was taking place a further station, known as a 'Repeater' would intercept all the short reports from each area and then re-broadcast them. This re-broadcast provided a significant source of daily intelligence, as each of the reporting station callsigns were identified within the re-broadcast traffic. In consequence the system employed by the German Air Force for the benefit of their high command was also to prove invaluable to the Royal Air Force, as it provided their command with the up-to-date status, on a daily basis, of the operational serviceability of all air stations in the Greater Reich.

A further additional task was a network that had first come under observation at Fort Bridgewoods on 7 February 1940, when increased activity on a number of German Air Force frequencies was noticed by the EWAs. What was of note was that during the transmission of traffic the pre-word WEL was transmitted followed by a number. Immediately following the transmission of WEL and its attendant number all further transmission ceased on that frequency. By scanning the band the EWAs established that the stations involved could then be found operating on another frequency. During observation of the new frequency the same process was followed, the pre-word WEL followed by a number was transmitted and the stations ceased transmitting, only to be found on yet another frequency. This rapid frequency changing tactic was observed to be in use by a large number of German wireless telegraphy stations and continued for a number of days in succession.

# Fort Bridgewoods

This new tactic of signals security was given the name of 'WEL COMPLEX' and it had not been entirely unexpected as there had been some earlier interception of unusual activity taking place when certain known air frequencies had seen a significant rise in traffic volumes between 4 and 6 February 1940, whilst traffic levels on the Luftgau short reporting groups had shown a consequential reduction in traffic. The operating frequencies observed were in the order of 3,000 to 6,500kHz, and from careful observation it was to be established that the WEL signal referred to specific alternative frequencies which were also to be identified by the EWAs. Subsequent intelligence, likely to have come from the early Ultra decrypts, that the allocation of alternative frequencies used in this signals security tactic were listed in the current edition of a German signals manual, A Fu Luft or Anordunungen fuer den Funkbetrieb der Luftwaffe, and that the extensive use that had come under observation by Fort Bridgewoods was likely to have been an exercise in preparation for a change of edition for that particular signals book. In a report prepared by Fort Brigewoods dated February 1940 it was strongly suggested that this particular use of the 'WEL COMPLEX' was a Lufgau organisational exercise which had been designed to test the resilience of the German wireless telegraphy network and to establish if they could maintain point–to-point communications during periods of wireless telegraphy interference and maintain maximum security from interception by the British 'Y' Service.

It was already established that the Germans used crystals to define their transmitter operating frequencies and for the stability of their transmissions. Their transmitters had rotary wafer-switches which permitted the selection of a number of alternative crystals, permitting the possibility for fast frequency changing by the operators. The Fort Bridgewoods report admitted that from their observations the German operators could indeed achieve fast frequency changes when ordered by the WEL pre-word and that this tactic could very well provide good signals security and an ability to avoid wireless telegraphy interception by those who were not in possession of the book.

On 8 April EWAs at Fort Bridgewoods first observed a group of two wireless telegraphy stations which they identified as being in the North West part of Germany. Their activity could have been involved with the build-up to the troop movements as it was observed that a single station in North West Germany was sending messages in a previously unidentified cypher at half hourly intervals.

Prior to 8 April 1940 there had been no observation of any wireless telegraphy traffic that could have given any advance warning of the German invasion of Norway and Denmark and indeed, once the operation had started, it was equally impossible to gain any significant intelligence as clearly the Germans had imposed wireless telegraphy silence upon all the forces engaged in the operation. The German networks already under observation had remained at their normal traffic levels and in consequence had not given any indication of any specific build-up prior to the invasion.

One of the chain of HF Direction Finding stations, this one at Lydd in Kent, used to locate stations under observation.
© War Office, MoD 2014.

As April drew to a close a German Air Force group, clearly located in Norway, was identified by the Fort

Bridgewoods EWAs. From April until the end of 1940 a number of German Air Force wireless telegraphy stations were identified and taken under observation by Fort Bridgewoods. All were located in Scandinavia. This observation, unfortunately, yielded very little in the way of military activity. However, continued observation of the Wehrkreis network of stations had seen an extension set of stations established in Denmark and this yielded regular quantities of intercepted material.

With the build-up of German troop movements towards the German border with Holland, particular watch was maintained to attempt to get early indications of the German intention to invade. On 10 May 1940 the interception of mobile wireless telegraphy units located to the South West of Aachen was probably the first indication of the German intention to cross the border into Holland. This unit was clearly serving a more senior unit which was operating from the area around Maastricht. EWAs were able to report a build-up of stations operating on the same frequency between 12 and 14 of May. On 11 May a new German military wireless telegraphy station was placed under observation. It was soon identified as being located in Amsterdam and that it formed part of a larger group which was being controlled from Paderborn. Other stations associated with this network were identified and believed to be located at Lippstadt and Bremen. Subsequently more stations were uncovered by the Fort Bridgewoods EWAs as being in the general vicinity of Amsterdam and that they were being controlled by a station located near Hanover. In all, Fort Bridgewoods was able to positively identify a large network of German wireless telegraphy stations in Holland, indeed on 15 May an EWA intercepted an important message which had been sent in the clear which told of the wounding of a high ranking military officer, General Student.

The wireless telegraphy procedures observed were consistent with those previously seen as part of the German 'lightning' style of invasion, with fast-moving mechanised infantry fanning out across the country. During the high-speed phase of the invasion much of the traffic was sent in clear, with just code words being used to mask the identity of units. That which was enciphered was masked in three letter codes and use was also made of transposition techniques. Due to the speed of the advance there was almost no use made of the high-grade Enigma code, and it was also clear that the previously observed use of radio silence had been made to mask the main occupying forces during this operation.

What was to follow was the invasion of France and the fallback of the British Expeditionary Force, following the capitulation of Belgium. Fort Bridgewoods was still heavily engaged with the primary role, taking German Air Force traffic in high-grade Enigma five-letter code. However, they were now to be faced with intercepting a large volume of wireless telegraphy traffic from the mobile units that formed the spearhead of the German advance. The traffic from these units was sent either as 'Klartext', clear text, or in a 'stencil' cipher. The clear text messages were normally reporting the positions of the forward detachments of the German Units engaged in the advance into France, but also reported the positions of the British troops as they were either holding or falling back towards the sea. The Germans were so sure of themselves they were even providing advance information about their own intentions back to their rear command areas. Although these intercepted messages were often to have little tactical value there was a

# Fort Bridgewoods

process in place for immediate onward transmission of these important intercepts to the War Office by direct telephone line. All this traffic was from lower formations of the German advance and in consequence there was very little instance of the high-grade Enigma code being used during this busy period of the Battle for France.

Fort Bridgewoods did identify one higher formation German group during this period and they were very active indeed, using both high-grade Enigma and transposition cyphers. Over 1,500 pieces of traffic were intercepted from this group during the invasion of France. One message that was sent in the clear was signed as coming from OBDL or the Commander in Chief, Air Force. The control for this group was located in or around Dortmund until about 1 June 1940. Thereafter it relocated to a forward position somewhere between Brussels and Liege. By 24 June this station had moved again, this time locating itself in Paris, where it was joined by a number of other wireless telegraphy stations serving important commands. As France was being occupied, a large number of German Air Force wireless telegraphy stations became active and by the close of 1940 many Air Groups were being intercepted at Fort Bridgewoods as part of the primary task on behalf of Bletchley Park, this task very much aiding the work on breaking high-grade Enigma material.

It was around the end of July 1940 that the intention to close the station at Fort Bridgewoods was mooted. This was precipitated by the proximity of the Fort to the coast, some 30 miles or so, where it was believed the Germans might soon attempt to invade. Other important stations were also relocated due to the invasion scare, including the radio research station where much of our continuing research on radar was being undertaken.

In August of 1940 the code-breakers of Bletchley Park were astonished to learn that the interception of Germany's wireless telegraphy signals was no longer to be carried out by the highly experienced EWAs at Fort Bridgewoods. The operation was to move Chicksands and thereafter to a new centre located in a country house in Bedfordshire, and that it would be manned by a new group of operators.

Despite their total lack of interest in hand-derived interception scripts in the low days of 1933/34, when Lt Beale was desperately trying to keep official interest in the work of Fort Bridgewoods, now the cryptographers were faced with a whole new set of circumstances.

**The main house at Bletchley Park, 1938. © GC&CS.**

A letter of protest was written on 26 August by Hugh Alexander, Gordon Welchman and Stuart Milner-Barry. The authors of the letter claimed that the move would be extremely dangerous and may well have disastrous effects on British code-breaking efforts. The problem, as they perceived it, was that the margin between breaking Enigma and failing to do so was already so slender because Enigma traffic was so light that the task of breaking the code was exceptionally difficult. In spite of the success already achieved by Bletchley Park, it was made very clear that breaking Enigma messages hung by a thread and any change in the provision of Enigma messages could snap that thread once and for all. Within the letter they cited a case that had taken place as recently as 5 May 1940, when they had been unable to work out the Enigma settings being used in Norway merely because there was a mistake in relation to one letter in the indicator group of one message. It turned out to be the vital link in the chain of evidence which, if taken down correctly by the intercept operator, could have made all the difference. They also stated that they had only broken the intercepted traffic for only half the days of September 1939, and the reason for that must have been that the recording of the message intercepted had been carried out incorrectly.

Their point could best be demonstrated by a recent example when, during one day, there were 267 messages. Only six were needed to break Enigma, yet if any one of the six had been missing, Enigma would not have broken on that day. The actual margin for error was often so small that the slightest reduction in the standards of interception might have proved fatal.

According to the letter writers, Fort Bridgewoods was obtaining the right answers four times out of five, whereas less experienced operators already operating at Shefford, another interception station, missed out callsigns altogether (the callsigns identified who was sending the message and to whom it was bound), and failed to give clear information about where the signals were coming from. Yet without the methods that Fort Bridgewoods employed so well, the crib method could not be successfully employed. In other words, without Fort Bridgewoods' expertise, Enigma could not be broken. One reason for this was that when German operators moved from one frequency to another, Fort Bridgewoods EWAs could hunt them down through knowing the peculiarities of the different operators. As we shall see later, the letter-writers were to prevail.

**Chicksands Priory, now the Officers' Mess of the Intelligence Corps, but in 1940 it was RAF Chicksands and the 'Y' station to which Fort Bridgewoods was to be moved in the interim, whilst its permanent home at Beaumanor was being completed. © MoD 2014.**

Amongst all the German Air Force traffic that was being intercepted at Fort Bridgewoods was that which came from a group of stations that were identified by the code name Brown and was associated with a particular cipher. The name Brown links directly back to Gordon Welchman who, whilst conducting his initial work on German enigma, was collecting discriminants and he was able to link particular ones with specific Enigma keys. The various keys he targeted were displayed using coloured pencils, Red, Green, Brown and so on.

It had been recognised very early on that this group of stations and the traffic that was being sent was going to prove very important, so its interception was given the highest priority. The stations that formed this particular wireless telegraphy network were known to be connected with radio research and experimentation associated with the German Air Force. What was more important was that from interception it had been established they were involved in the use of special apparatus which used radio beams for bombing. This was clearly very important at the time, as this was the period of the great raids of the Blitz of 1940 running into 1941.

# Fort Bridgewoods

**One of the beam-flying HE111's of KG 100, taken from the cockpit of one of the other squadron members.** © Luft Archiv.

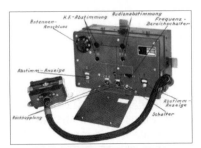

**German blind landing receiver EBL-1.** © German Air Force, Bundesarchiv.

**Knickebein aerial array.** © German Air Force, Bundesarchiv.

The interception of this group of stations was to provide a vital insight into what Churchill was to call 'the wizard war' or the battle of the beams. This particular line of intelligence was vital to the work of Dr R V Jones, who argued the use of radio beams by the German Air Force as an aid to accurate bombing, and who subsequently identified the existence of several forms of beam stations and beam flyers who acted as 'pathfinders' for other formations of bombers. The first beam arrangement identified was a system known as Knickebein. This was followed by X Geräte and then Y Geräte. The aircraft initially involved with this system was KG26 and later KG100.

The vital thing about this system was that it did not actually require any new equipment to operate the beams. The system used the EBL-1 blind-landing receiver, which was just 'hotted' up by the engineers. The system relied upon being able to accurately locate a beam signal over the target, which had dots on one side of the beam and dashes on the other. When you were in the middle of the beam the pilot could hear a continuous tone in his headphones.

A second cross-beam on another frequency had the same configuration and this provided the warning when approaching the target. The photograph left shows the EBL-1 blind landing receiver as fitted into the HE111. Blind landing was not an unknown technique, indeed the Royal Air Force had been undertaking development work prior to the war at Boscombe Down.

The Knickebein aerial array was mounted on a turntable, to enable the beam to be made fully directional. The aerial comprised two directional elements which were angled a few degrees apart, thus creating the tight focus to the beam that was finally transmitted.

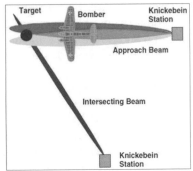

**The Knickebein beam bombing system.**

This particular group of German wireless telegraphy stations, in contrast to other German operators, had very poor radio security discipline and poor operating procedures. Indeed these operators consistently broke all the rules, with personal 'chatter', use of name, locations and even the ciphers in use. All of this was more that gratefully recorded by the

EWAs at Fort Bridgewoods.

The inappropriate use of operator's names was so evident that it was easy to identify individual stations on a daily basis, despite the required daily regime of callsign change being in place. On one very special occasion, recorded by the operators at Fort Bridgewoods, there was the transmission of a complete Enigma wheel setting and rotor order for the day. It was this kind of basic cryptosecurity error that was so vital to the code-breakers of Bletchley Park and the Fort Bridgewoods EWAs were only to happy to oblige with high quality interception work to provide this to them.

The use of radio beams to mark targets over England meant that the Germans could bomb accurately on any night, no matter what the cloud cover or state of the moon. Initially the Royal Air Force would not accept the need for the Germans to use beams to aid their bombing, as they could not see past their long-held view that bombing could be achieved to a highly accurate standard by the use of astro-navigation. Subsequent surveys proved that astro-navigation was in no way accurate, because about the best that could be achieved was a fix within five miles of the predicted location. These surveys went on to prove that British bombing was in the main totally inaccurate, with many raids not even hitting the correct target. Bomber Command was to move to beam flying themselves later in the war and also introduce highly effective pathfinder squadrons which utilized a system code named Oboe.

The interception of Brown by the EWAs of Fort Bridgewoods provided much of the important intelligence that permitted Dr R V Jones to unravel all three systems and allow the development of countermeasures which made them effectively useless once properly deployed.

One of the first real clues that Dr R V Jones had came directly from an Enigma decrypt which read: 'KNICKEBEIN, KLEVE, IST AUF PUNKT 53 GRAD 24 MINUTEN NORD UND EIN GRAD WEST EINGERICHTET'. When translated this means 'Kleve (Cleves) Knickebein is established at position 53 degrees 24 minutes North and one degree West'.

This was sufficient for Jones and he managed to get the Prime Minister's approval for a reconnaissance flight to search for a beam on that heading over England, based upon a starting point of Cleves. The beam was eventually found as the flight passed over Retford. Its heading pointed directly over the all important Rolls Royce Aero Engine factory at Derby. The rest of this story belongs to Dr R V Jones, who describes this and other scientific intelligence matters in his most excellent book *Most Secret War*.

**The German bombing of London during the Blitz of 1940.**
© **German Air Force, Bundesarchiv.**

# Fort Bridgewoods

This particular group had been first spotted by the EWAs of Fort Bridgewoods in 1939, during Hitler's assault upon Poland. Identified by the callsigns POL and 9WE, thereafter it was known as the POL-9WE group. Prior to the fall of France, Fort Bridgewoods identified this group in Berlin, Koethen (control), Luneburg, Glogau, Neubrandenburg, Markisch, Lubeck and Friedland. It became highly active in August 1940 and remained so for the remainder of the year. A noticeable feature of the traffic from this group was the large number of KR or Urgent Messages that it transmitted between Boulogne and Vannes in high-grade Enigma Brown cipher, and occasionally the Red key.

The messages in the high-grade Red key were highly sought after by the operators at Fort Bridgewoods, as the length and time of the transmissions aided the prediction, with uncanny accuracy, of whether or not an air raid would take place that night. It was also possible to establish from the general characteristics of the message if the raid was to be on London, in which case the operators at Fort Bridgewoods would be in for a noisy night.

As Christmas 1940 arrived, the Fort Bridgewoods EWAs were able to predict from operator 'chatter' that there would be three days free from bombing. They also identified, again from indiscreet operator 'chatter', that KG100 was indeed a beam flying squadron.

Shortly before the night of 7 September 1940, when the nightly bombing of London commenced, Dr R V Jones received a telephone call at home in the early hours of the morning. The call was from Professor 'Bimbo' Norman, who worked in Hut 3 at Bletchley Park. Norman was a professor of German and worked in Hut 3, translating and collating intelligence from the decrypts of German Air Force traffic which been broken through the work carried out in Hut 6. Norman was well aware of the areas of intelligence work being conducted by R V Jones and accordingly was constantly on the lookout for anything that might assist him in his task.

Norman had identified something new from an Enigma decrypt and whilst he did not know its meaning he felt quite sure that it was a matter for Jones. On the strength of the call Jones agreed to travel to Bletchley that morning. His time was certainly not wasted.

The codebreakers of Bletchley Park had broken into a new line of traffic in which there was a mention of beams, including one that was eight to ten seconds arc in 20,000, which would suggest that this beam would be no wider that 20 yards at a distance of 200 miles from its point of origin. Jones also noted that the term X-Geräte ( X Apparatus) was being fitted into an aircraft with the callsign 6N+LK and that this was one which belonged to KG100. Dr Jones was quickly able to cross-reference this with other intelligence that had already been supplied to him by Flt Lt Rowley Scott-Farnie, a pre war radio amateur (G5FI), that suggested that beams were being monitored on frequencies around 70MHz which were being radiated from the Cherbourg and Calais areas.

Dr Jones promptly asked for priority to be given to the interception and attack of this new line of Enigma high-grade cipher, and his request was well judged.

On 24 October 1940, upon the advice of Dr Jones, Professor Linderman sent a minute to Churchill indicating that there was good reason to believe that a new method was to be adopted by the German Air Force to send a few KG100 aircraft fitted with special devices to assist in blind-bombing operations to start fires on targets that aircraft not so fitted can use as aiming points for their bomb loads. It is perhaps very interesting to note that around this time Milch, Head of the Luftwaffe, was giving advice to Goering that the current policy of night attacks was useless without the special radio beam equipment and that it was his further recommendation that KG100 should receive priority in both personnel and aircraft, also that attacks would be possible even on the darkest nights or through cloud.

On 28 May 1940 one particular task allotted to Fort Bridgewoods was to monitor German Air Force stations working on 4131 and 4370kHz. The control station, German Air Head Quarters, transmitted a number of short KR, urgent messages which commenced with 'Sofort Stuka', to outstations which were intercepted by the EWAs and quickly identified as tasking Stuka dive bombers to map references which corresponded to locations at Dunkirk, where the British Expeditionary Force was being evacuated from the beaches. This was Operation Dynamo, devised and executed by Vice Admiral Ramsey at Dover and using every ship available, including all the little ships that he could muster, from paddle steamers to pleasure yachts. One of those many little pleasure yachts was 'Sundowner', owned and skippered by Cdr Lightoller. He was a veteran Destroyer Captain of the Great War, but perhaps better known as the most senior surviving officer of RMS Titanic.

**Commander Charles Lightoller DSC and Bar RD RNR. Senior surviving officer of RMS Titanic and owner of 'Sundowner', the Dunkirk little ship that he commanded during the evacuation.**
**© Cdr Lightoller.**

Lightoller and his young volunteer crew of Scouts braved the ferocity of the dive bombing at Dunkirk and rescued many soldiers of the BEF from the beaches, bringing them safely back to Dover in nothing more than what they stood up in. Dynamo was a great success as an evacuation and its importance was not lost on General Eisenhower who, as Supreme Commander Allied Forces, employed Vice Admiral Ramsey to organise the Armada that took the Allied troops to the D Day beaches.

Ellingworth was promptly made aware of the nature of these transmissions and their implication for the British Expeditionary Force which was trapped with their backs to the sea at Dunkirk. An urgent request was made of the military high command for permission to conduct jamming of the German stations, to cause havoc with the command and control arrangements for the Stuka squadrons who were dive bombing the troops on the beaches and the ships that were conducting the evacuation. Within the space of a few hours Ellingworth was informed that a high power transmitter located at Rugby was being made available for military control at Fort Bridgewoods, so that jamming could be commenced forthwith. By the early afternoon a direct telephone line had been installed from GPO Headquarters to Fort Bridgewoods, with the line terminated directly alongside the intercept operator's receiver.

# Fort Bridgewoods

The MF/HF transmitter hall at Rugby. It was here that a high power transmitter was allocated to Fort Bridgewoods, to jam the GAF command and control radio link to the Stuka dive bombers who were attacking the troops on the Dunkirk beaches. © GPO.

Rugby High Power CW and Phone transmitter hall. © GPO.

Whilst Fort Bridgewoods was technically now ready to jam the command and control wireless telegraphy network for the marauding Stukas, pressure was placed upon Ellingworth to hold fire, as diplomatically it would not be right to commence jamming without the prior agreement of the French, Belgians and the Royal Air Force. What really raised Ellingworth's hackles was the fact that gaining this agreement was likely to take two whole days, during which time British and French lives were being lost on the beaches.

Whilst the political wrangling between military high command, the French, Belgians and Royal Air Force was getting underway, Lt Cdr Ellingworth was losing his patience with the situation and was not prepared to countenance any further delay and wasted lives for the want of jamming not being commenced. As a retired Royal Navy officer, Ellingworth was well aware of the precedence set by Nelson at the Battle of Copenhagen in 1801, when he ignored his Admiral's signals by putting his telescope to his blind eye, and with the words 'I see no signal' continued the engagement of the enemy and won a glorious victory. Like Nelson before him Ellingworth chose to act, and having an appalling lapse of memory commenced jamming when the next wave of Stuka attacks was ordered by the command station.

The impact on the German control operator of 25 kilowatts of jamming with raw inverted speech interference emanating from Rugby on his exact frequency was instant. He lost control of the Stukas he was directing. Frantic attempts were made by the controller to order a frequency change. but to no avail. The jamming signal was simply too intense.

These log made by EWAs at the time illustrate the success of the jamming:

28/05/40. 4131kHz successfully jammed from 2145 to 0000 GMT, when control station made the pre-word WEL and shifted frequency. Control station became so confused that he lost control of his group and asked stations individually who they were. Control station resorted to calling CQ, thus giving away his identity as the controlling authority. Interference reported by control station as being strength 5 (this being the optimum figure used by German radio operators)

29/05/40. Jamming from 0000 to 1900 GMT on 4131kHz and 4370kHz. Control station has carried out several frequency changes from 4131 to 4370 and back again. During the frequency changes the controller has managed to get a few messages to outstations. Rugby taking from between three and five minutes to achieve a frequency change. Germans taking just five seconds to achieve their change of frequency.

30/05/40. Control of 4131 and 4370 jammed frequencies. Has made two or three clear text messages, asking for reports. Control has apparently adopted tactic of producing a second control station that transmits traffic to himself on an alternative frequency, in an attempt to get us to jam the wrong frequency. Also sends traffic on both frequencies whilst Rugby is making a frequency change. Jamming continued on non decoy frequency unless it becomes certain that the control station has indeed shifted. It is believed that this tactic has been arranged through another network using high-grade Enigma.

Despite the best attempt of the German operators, the skill and observation of the EWAs at Fort Bridgewoods was showing through. The operators at Fort Bridgewoods were clearly able to judge the effectiveness of their jamming from what they were able to discern from their own receivers, and as they perceived the Germans had shifted their frequency in the slightest to try and avoid the jamming, Rugby was tasked with the same change and the suppression of the German signals went on like a game of cat and mouse.

The GPO staff at Rugby proved magnificent throughout the whole of this operation, ensuring that all the frequency changing, aerial changes and retuning of transmitters was carried out with absolute efficiency. This was no easy task when dealing with such high-powered equipment. Their contribution to this operation was vital and they did not let the operators at Fort Bridgewoods down. This was certainly one of the very first jamming operations of World War II, and those on the beaches at Dunkirk would have been extremely grateful had they known about the most secret war that was being conducted from an old fort on the North Downs overlooking the Medway Valley. As for the EWAs, well they had certainly stood up to the task with all the professionalism that had come to be expected from them. Getting them to stand down as their watches came to an end had become an almost impossible task for the shift supervisors as many of them, being old soldiers, had scented the smell of battle. It was perhaps a good thing that all the operators were male, as the language in the set room was often quite fruity when the German controller failed to sneak traffic past the jamming, or if he managed to get one or two messages through during the short delays of a frequency change.

Fort Bridgewoods was also tasked with the interception of wireless telegraphy traffic which was clearly not military in nature. A short but intense period of observation of a German police wireless telegraphy network was undertaken between 25 July and 31 July. This network had been previously identified and this current observation was to establish if there had been any addition of stations. The observation was confined to the medium frequency band, specifically 152kHz, 155kHz and 410kHz, with the main control station identified as being located in Berlin. The Berlin control station used two frequencies to maintain regular communications with sub-control stations in provincial areas. These sub control stations each had a group of minor stations which they communicated with using

# Fort Bridgewoods

410kHz. The sub-control stations used different callsigns when operating with the minor stations to those which they used when reporting to the main control station in Berlin.

The observation period identified that little had changed with these stations, but a good volume of traffic was being exchanged. Fort Bridgewoods, from its observation, were able to provide a report upon the nature of the traffic and their operating procedures. This was to prove most valuable as the German police network rapidly expanded into the occupied lands of Europe.

In the latter part of 1939 and into early 1940 Fort Bridgewoods undertook an intensive observation of Russian wireless telegraphy stations, but owing to more pressing tasks, observation was confined, in the main, to groups of stations known to be operating on the Finland front. This work was confined to the night watches only, when other observation tasks became less active. A high volume of traffic was intercepted and detailed information was taken on the frequencies and how they were used, also the callsigns in use and operating procedure signals. Although the operating procedures and procedure signals were as complex as ever, their advantage in signals security was lost by an appalling lack of wireless telegraphy discipline on the part of the Russian operators.

One particular Russian message intercepted at Fort Bridgewoods was in plain language and read as follows: 'On arrival of the enemy our battalion turned and fled'!

The possibility of invasion, as has already been discussed, raised the question of the evacuation of Fort Bridgewoods to move it well beyond the immediate invasion area. We have already seen the concerns raised by the code-breakers at Bletchley Park about any threat to the provision of Enigma traffic interception, which could seriously damage the ability of Bletchley Park to continue to break existing Enigma keys and carry out observation of others to gain any chance of breaks in the future. The protection of the Fort Bridgewoods capability was far too important to allow it to remain at threat and consequently a plan was put in place to move in the interim to Chicksands Priory near Shefford and thereafter on to Beaumanor Hall.

The actual transfer of operations took place on 14 February 1941. A small advance party had set off some days before to ensure continuity of interception. The main body of staff was transported in coaches hired from the Maidstone and District Bus Company.

The move did not go well, as despite all the meticulous planning, upon arrival there was no allocation of accommodation. Ellingworth had to pacify his EWAs by sending them into the local public house and paying for several rounds of drinks, while he went off with

**A motor coach of the type provided by Maidstone and District Bus Company during the move of personnel from Fort Bridgewoods to Chicksands.**
© **Maidstone and District Bus Company.**

the local policeman and billeting officer to try and coerce local residents into opening their doors to the men from Kent.

One of the lighter, but serious moments surrounding the move to Chicksands was recounted by Signalman Len Moore in his memoir entitled *Z17*, which was his operator identity, where he recounts how when arriving late at night and with no light allowed in the motor coach he managed to lose his Lee Enfield rifle! Following a number of enquiries and letters to the Maidstone and District Bus Company the rifle was finally found in the lost property office at the Gillingham depot.

# Chapter 8.
# Victorian fort and wooden huts – the Ultra secret

Shortly after the Munich crisis of late September 1938, Gordon Welchman received a note offering him a position from Alistair Denniston, Head of the GC&CS, to which he replied in the affirmative. Shortly after this exchange he was called to London for a short period of indoctrination into manual methods of cryptography and into a number of machine based cipher systems that were in use at the time.

Gordon Welchman.
© Gordon Welchman.

Welchman recalls in his book *The Hut Six Story* that he had the distinct impression that the chances of ever being able to do anything with the German Enigma traffic was at the time considered minimal, at least until access to a machine could be achieved.

**The Cottage, as it looked in 2008 when the author visited Bletchley Park.**

On the morning of the declaration of war with Germany, September 1939, Gordon Welchman made his way by car from Cambridge to Bletchley Park and reported directly to Denniston. Welchman, fresh from academic life and with no understanding of communications and cryptography, was put to work with Dilly Knox in The Cottage, which was located in the stable yard of Bletchley Park.

Amongst other academics drawn to Bletchley Park on the outbreak of war he found Alan Turing of Kings College Cambridge, a brilliant mathematician. Knox at this time was in charge of the British attack on the German Enigma machine. Turing, although brilliant and clearly the man for the moment, was openly homosexual. This was to cause serious issues about his security status in later years, indeed he was to commit suicide whilst in his mid 40's.

Welchman was soon moved on to Elmers School, adjacent to the park, where he started a study of callsigns and discriminants, made up of groups of letters and figures. These were regular features of the traffic that had already been intercepted, in particular by the War Office wireless interception station located at Fort Bridgewoods. The latter was referred to as Chatham by the code breakers, due to its close proximity to the naval town of that name.

**Alan Turing, from a passport photograph. © Alan Turing.**

This highly efficient and very secret organisation, hidden within the thick walls of the old Victorian Fort, had for some time been intercepting German wireless telegraphy traffic with an identifiable signature comprising five-letter groups. These five-letter groups were consistent with the output of the German Enigma machine. So far little use had been made of their output. The accumulated product of each day's interception was bundled up and sent to Bletchley Park, along with a report of the day's traffic. This accumulation of traffic was made available to Gordon Welchman and Gordon Kendrick by Colonel John Tiltman, who at the time was in charge of Army operations at Bletchley Park.

A typical message was made up of a number of elements within an unencrypted preamble, which was followed directly by encrypted text arranged in five letter groups. A typical message transmitted by a German operator would be intercepted thus:

DF8 8QT DE D6K (to and from callsigns)
1450              (time of origin)
128               (number of letters)
Part I of 3      (single or multi part message)
QKZ             (discriminant)
DON            (indicator setting)
BT
WQSEU PMPIZ TLJJU WQEHG LRBID
FEWBO JIEPD JZAHT TBJRO AHHYO
JYGSF HYKTN TDBPH ULKOH UNTIM
OFARL BPAPM XKZZX DTSXL QWHVL
RAGUZ ZTSGG YIJV
BT

**The thick concrete walls of Fort Bridgewoods, that provided protection to the interception operations.**
**© Dr Philip Blenkinsop.**

# Fort Bridgewoods

Added to the intercepted German transmission would be the remarks of the EWA as follows:

4760KCs (frequency in use)
1100 (time of interception)

The operators at Chatham would have some prior warning that a message was to be sent by the German operator, as the station would be operating in a net with a control station. The control station would make the necessary prior transmissions for traffic to be passed and consequently the EWAs at Chatham would have ample opportunity to record time, frequency and callsigns in advance of the preamble being sent. All Chatham intercepts were hand written exactly as taken by the EWA. On occasions the EWA would be unsure about the accuracy of a particular Morse character and alternatives would be recorded, perhaps where the signal received was weak or where there was heavy noise from atmospheric static (QRN). Where the intercept was garbled and parts had been missed, the EWA would provide an estimate of the number or groups believed to have been missed.

Both Welchman and Kendrick started work on the Chatham intercepts, but neither had any real sense of direction and simply made lists of items within the traffic, eventually coming across things that seemed to be of some significance and interest. Soon after this first start at examining the Chatham traffic Kendrick was moved to other work and Welchman was left to soldier on alone.

**The counterscarp gallery set into the outer wall of the deep moat.**
**© Graham French.**

Shortly after Kendrick's transfer to other duties, Welchman was handed a small batch of decoded messages by Josh Cooper who headed Air Force operations. There was not much to this traffic, perhaps two or three days worth at the very most. Such was the secrecy that surrounded this work, not even Welchman was made aware of how it had been obtained. Whilst a study of this material did not move him any further forward, it did provide an insight into what his work was to be in the coming months, perhaps even years. One thing that the early research carried out by Welchman did establish was a clear understanding that associated with each Enigma key would be four three letter groups. These were know as discriminants, examples being: KQV LMY GJR ABO

The discriminant was not part of the key but would appear in the preamble of the message, that is to say unencrypted. The discriminant provided the indications of which particular key the Enigma machine had been set up for. Put simply it permitted the receiving cipher clerk to be able to identify which Enigma key the sending operator had used to encode this particular message.

Whilst the Chatham intercepts were still quite unreadable to Welchman, they did provide him with a detailed study of callsigns, radio frequencies, times of interception and the use of discriminants for each day. Welchman was soon able to group discriminants of the day for keys in use, looking to establish all four in use for the particular Enigma key. Having made the identification these were then transferred to a chart using coloured pencils, red, blue and green. This early start provided a format that was to remain in use and virtually unchanged for the remainder of the war. The colours also stuck, in particular RED, a key that was to provide significant intelligence in many areas of operation and very often providing a basis of attack on other Enigma keys.

GREEN traffic appeared only sporadically amongst the Chatham intercepts, but a study of French intercepted traffic soon established that this was traffic from a German Army administrative network. It was not an easy interception opportunity for Chatham, as it was sent on MF frequencies and consequently did not have a significant range of travel from the transmitting station. Analysis of the callsigns associated with GREEN soon established that they were repeating each month and Welchman was soon able to provide Chatham with predictions of those it should expect to find each day on GREEN networks.

With this work well in hand, Welchman believed that it was high time he made the journey to visit the Fort Bridgewoods station. A firm friendship was immediately established between Welchman and Ellingworth, who was the Officer in Charge at Fort Bridgewoods. Ellingworth introduced Welchman to many of the technical aspects of interception work, areas of understanding that were vital if Welchman were to make further progress in this field. Welchman describes Ellingworth as a tower of strength and that he remained so throughout the war years. Welchman's welcome was typical of that provided by the navy and included a full tour of the station and introduction to the EWAs who were the very source of the traffic that Welchman had been analysing and developing. He was able to watch the EWAs at work, which underscored the high opinion that Welchman had already formed of this highly industrious group. Ellingworth introduced Welchman to the characteristics of short wave radio and many of the problems faced by his EWAs in their work to intercept weak Morse code signals from distant stations. Ellingworth also identified to Welchman something that R V Jones was also vigorously complaining about; that the state of British frequency measurement was not exact and left much to be desired. Both transmitters and receivers of the day were subject to drift and consequently the intercept frequencies could well be recorded differently for the same radio net.

Also identified were the problems caused by the need to hunt around for stations

Lt Cdr M J W Ellingworth DSM RN Rtd, in the uniform of a Lieutenant Colonel Royal Signals, a rank he was afforded as the War Office could not cope with a Royal Navy officer being in charge of their principal Wireless Interception station.
© Howard Jellings.

and the fact that it was all too easy to intercept a nearby network. The effectiveness of the Fort Bridgewoods EWAs rested upon their ability to identify the known German nets from the individual operating characteristics of the funkers, something that was an acquired art. Some of the Fort Bridgewoods EWAs were described by Welchman as being quite phenomenal, with the extraordinary

# Fort Bridgewoods

combination of brain and hearing that made possible the reception of weak and marginal signals that would have otherwise been missed by any automated reception technique.

The visit to Fort Bridgewoods proved most fruitful for Welchman and by the close of the day he and Ellingworth had agreed a procedure that was to endure throughout the remainder of the war years, with a regular register of all intercepted Enigma traffic taken at Fort Bridgewoods being sent directly to Bletchley Park. The traffic analysts at Fort Bridgewoods were already heavily committed and had no time to undertake the analytical work being completed by Welchman. Consequently, it was agreed by Ellingworth that the preamble plus the first two five letter groups of all intercepted messages would be sent directly by teleprinter. The only delay would be that of sufficient traffic being collected to make the teleprinter transmission worthwhile. This was to be known by Welchman as the traffic register. In turn Welchman agreed with Ellingworth that he would call Fort Bridgewoods each day by telephone once sets of discriminants had been identified. Welchman also provided all predictions of callsigns and more importantly would suggest which traffic appeared to be of particular interest. Thus was born the process of co-operation between interceptors and Bletchley Park that was to become so critical as the Ultra intelligence source was developed.

Each day entries were made on a frequency/time chart by Patricia Newman, who had been appointed as the first assistant to Welchman. This work was completed as the traffic registers arrived over the teleprinter link from Fort Bridgewoods. This chart was about the size of an average office desktop and as the RED, BLUE AND GREEN discriminants for the day were identified they would be placed onto the chart in coloured pencil. The discriminants would also be telephoned directly to Fort Bridgewoods. The process also allowed the identification of other traffic that was not routinely being monitored by the Chatham EWAs, and by the process of close cooperation and frequent telephone calls between Welchman and Ellingworth the EWAs were directed to take specific traffic in order to permit more thorough investigation. This process added BROWN and ORANGE to the RED, BLUE and GREEN traffic that was already being routinely taken by Fort Bridgewoods EWAs. This process permitted the identification of the various elements and groupings within the German military command structures that were using the same Enigma machine but different keys.

Throughout 1939 Welchman remained the only link between Fort Bridgewoods and the code breakers at Bletchley Park. As work developed at Bletchley Park and more frequent breaks were made into the various traffic streams an organisation was developed by Welchman within Hut 6 where both Army and Air Force traffic was attacked. The resulting breaks were sent for assessment in Hut 3, thus providing a complementary process from interception through to dissemination of the intelligence products. Amongst those working within the Hut 3 organisation was Professor of Ger-

**Hut Six Bletchley Park, where the product from Fort Bridgewoods was decrypted.**

Professor of German, Fredrick 'Bimbo' Norman, who worked as a translator and intelligence officer in Hut 3. Norman was vital to the work of Dr R V Jones, 'spotting' vital clues during the Battle of the Beams. © R V Jones.

man Frederick 'Bimbo' Norman, who became the vital link, as principal researcher, with Dr R V Jones who had been appointed as an Assistant Director of Intelligence – ADI (Science) – to ensure that scientific intelligence was being properly developed. Jones played a vital role in establishing the German Air Force's use of radio beams to provide accurate bombing, both at night and in difficult conditions. He also developed vital intelligence in respect of the German use of radar and development of the V1 and V2 revenge weapons.

Whilst Norman in Hut 3 was providing Jones with vital intelligence, it was the EWAs at Fort Bridgewoods who were providing this invaluable opportunity, as they were intercepting the traffic associated with both the command and control structures of these organisations and the research units developing the new weapons systems.

The daily traffic lists were received into Hut 6 and from midnight onwards each day three copies of the list were produced and studied by the registration room, intercept control room and the machine room. From the traffic sheets the registration room would seek to determine the sets of discriminants for the various keys. The intercept room, making full use of the charts in the registration room, would set about focusing the interception effort and ensuring that the interception resources were tasked to the traffic streams that were most wanted by the code breakers. The machine room would identify which key was most amenable to a break for that day and consequently the interception focus would move to that particular task, say the RED key would be given priority over the effort on BLUE. As the code breakers became more adept at their work it was quite common for RED to break in the early hours of the morning watch.

As the process became more established and effective, Welchman invited Ellingworth to pay a return visit and accordingly a night was spent watching the code breaking process in play. At around one o'clock in the morning a shout of triumph was heard and a visit to the decoding room permitted, Ellingworth to get his first sight of the decodes of the previous days traffic being decrypted on the TypeX machines that were modified to mirror the Enigma machine process.

Welchman and Ellingworth spent the night in Hut 6, and Ellingworth was able to get a full briefing on the work carried out there. Discussions took place around the problems in handling Enigma traffic. One area of discussion was the message texts that were intercepted by Fort Bridgewoods and other intercept stations. Following Welchman's first visit to Fort Bridgewoods a protocol had been established whereby a traffic register was transmitted to Bletchley Park. This register contained all the information necessary to break an Enigma key: the preamble, its discriminant, indicator setting and the first two groups of the message text which was known to contain the encrypted text setting or indicator. Following the breaking of the key, Bletchley Park needed intercepted mes-

# Fort Bridgewoods

sages for decrypting, and these were the very product being provided by the EWAs of Fort Bridgewoods on the standard message forms which in turn were bundled together and transported to Bletchley Park by dispatch rider.

Ellingworth and Welchman discussed in some detail how bundles of intercepted messages could be delivered from Fort Bridgewoods to Bletchley Park in a more timely manner, to reduce the time from interception to decryption. The existing teleprinter link was in no way adequate to cope with the work, so motorcycle dispatch riders remained the order of the day. They provided a first class, if not fully recognised service.

Discussion also turned to a method of giving particular messages priority and, for this limited number of messages, the teleprinter network was used. This brought about the term 'Welchman Special'. From the observation of the traffic lists provided by Fort Bridgewoods, Hut 6 could often establish particular messages that could prove to be of specific interest to the intelligence teams. An example would be traffic passed on a particular radio circuit, which could be heard regularly each day and had the same time of origin. These would often prove to be daily situation reports or daily commands to subordinate units, which proved to have great intelligence value. Where such traffic was identified by Bletchley Park it was agreed with Ellingworth that a call would be placed to the Head of Watch at Fort Bridgewoods, for that particular message to be given special handling. In consequence it would be immediately transmitted over the direct teleprinter link to Bletchley Park.

As a consequence of Ellingworth's visit to Welchman at Hut 6, the term 'Welchman Special' was introduced by Fort Bridgewoods to signify any such message that was to be afforded special handling. The use of the Welchman name was a sure indicator of the close and happy personal relationship that had been established with Fort Bridgewoods in late 1939 and cemented by Ellingworth's visit in early 1940.

During the same period an arm of Military Intelligence, MI8, carried out traffic analysis on the German radio nets that were under observation at Fort Bridgewoods. German networks were established with a control station and a number of outstations. To maintain these nets there was always an undercurrent of operator

**Hut 3 at Bletchley Park, where decrypted messages were translated and intelligence developed.**

'chatter', to maintain frequency and other aspects of control. The EWAs at Fort Bridgewoods logged all aspects of the German 'service traffic' and the resulting product was studied and analysed by the MI8 personnel. One of the important objectives of this group was establishing the callsign regime and breaking into the yearly callsign book as issued by both the German Army and Air Force. This work permitted an understanding of callsign allocations and consequently allowed for the identification of enemy units through their radio traffic. In this way the deployment and subsequent movements of specific units could be established and tracked.

# Victorian fort and wooden huts - the Ultra secret

From the very origins of Hut 6, through the establishing of the intelligence arm in Hut 3, the close co-operation with the interceptors of Fort Bridgewoods had permitted a dynamic and effective intelligence machine to be established.

In late 1940 the decision was taken to move the Chatham EWAs away from Fort Bridgewoods, something that caused considerable disquiet for Welchman and his organisation. Despite the protests of Welchman that the vital work of Chatham could be lost, the move took place in March 1941, first to Chicksands and thereafter to the newly-established station at Beaumanor. This new station at Beaumanor had been purpose built and permitted the deployment of rhombic aerials. These had much improved gain and directional properties, something that was never possible within the confined space of Fort Bridgewoods. With the move came the deployment of the American National HRO receivers and subsequently the RCA AR88, a Rolls Royce of a receiver also from an American stable.

Welchman visited Ellingworth at Beaumanor on a number of occasions and established that his band of Chatham EWAs, now joined by a swelling rank of ATS intercept operators, were just as impressive and professional as had been the case when located at Fort Bridgewoods.

It was on one of these occasions that Ellingworth told Welchman one of his organisational secrets, Fort Bridgewoods was by no means defunct as an interception station! Whilst designated as a training station for EWAs, Ellingworth maintained a small group of intercept operators there in order to achieve what he referred to as 'diversified reception'; that is to say where signals were weak and marginal at Beaumanor they could be taken at Fort Bridgewoods, where they may be more audible. Thus there was a clear interplay between the now primary station at Beaumanor and the small intercept enclave at Fort Bridgewoods. This disclosure by Ellingworth clearly established why such a master of the art of manual Morse as Retired Chief Petty Officer Telegraphist Albert Stevens was deployed at Fort Bridgewoods as chief instructor. Not relegation to a quiet backwater, but strategically deployed to fulfill a significant role within Ellingworth's interception organisation.

# Chapter 9.
# The night the bomb fell

From a Royal Air Force official report of German bombing operations over the Home Counties on the night of 16 October 1940 it is known that Fort Bridgewoods was one of the many locations that suffered bomb damage and fatalities. The report gives details as follows:

Rochester: An attack was made at 21:42 hours and damage was done to part of Fort Bridgewoods Wireless Station, where casualties were reported. Bombs are also reported to have fallen in the airport field and Fort Borstal.

This was not the first time that the German Air Force had targeted the area, which is not surprising given the proximity of the Shorts factory and Pobjoy Engineering, which were both located on the Rochester Airfield site and engaged in the production of the Short Stirling bomber.

On Friday 9 August 1940 Rochester airfield had been targeted for a very heavy raid, with six Short Stirling bombers destroyed just as they had come off of the production line.

On Thursday 15 August 1940 a force of 30 Dornier 17's of KG3 attacked Rochester airfield, with bombs falling across the runway, hangers and amongst a group of parked aircraft. A large clutch of high-explosive fragmentation bombs fell into the aircraft factory at the northern end of the site and these were interspersed with incendiary and delayed-action bombs. A number of vital stores were also destroyed, thus effectively delaying the vital production of the Stirling bombers. The KG3 flyers took aerial

**At least two of the heavily damaged Short Stirlings inside the factory hanger building, following an attack on the Rochester Airport site.**
**© Shorts Brothers, Rochester.**

reconnaissance photographs during the raid, which showed bombs falling across the Maidstone Road close to Fort Horsted. Some of the bombs from this raid fell in the fields close to Fort Bridgewoods.

Saturday 24 August 1940 saw another raid on Rochester Airfield, targeting the Shorts factory.

Monday 2 September 1940 saw heavy raids by the German Air Force on the airfields in the home counties, including the one at Rochester.

**Aerial photograph taken from a German bomber, during a raid on Rochester aerodrome. Fort Horsted can be seen at the top left of the Photograph.**
**© German Air Force, Bundesarchiv.**

On Wednesday 4 September 1940 the Germans returned in force, to carry out an attack on Pobjoy Engineering, a subsidiary of Short Brothers where engines and other vital components were manufactured.

It has already been seen that Fort Bridgewoods had suffered one earlier period of interruption to their interception activities, when a bomb falling in a nearby field had severed the main power supply to the station and put them off air for just over four hours.

On Wednesday 16 October the main raids for the night focused on London and its suburbs. During the raids three Luftwaffe aircraft were confirmed as destroyed and one as badly damaged. The casualties for that night were officially listed as follows:

London – 40 killed and 209 injured.
Other – 24 killed, 44 badly injured and 46 slightly injured.

At Fort Bridgewoods security patrols and fire watching were carried out by the station's own Home Guard detachment, designated 2nd Battalion, Kent Home Guard. In an official report of the tragic activities that unfolded at Fort Bridgewoods that night the Zone Controller commended the prompt and brave action of Section Commander T S G Worster of the Rochester Battalion of the Home Guard.

At 21:35 hours on the night of 16 October yet another raid was underway, with the likely target again being the Shorts works at Rochester Airfield. At this time the Luftwaffe tactic was to attack the Royal Air Force on the ground, in an attempt to destroy aircraft, make airfields unserviceable and destroy sites of aircraft production.

The target is believed not to have been the wireless interception station, as what hit the fort was just one bomb from a larger stick which had fallen elsewhere. It is likely that in the fog of the air battle the German bomb aimer had laid his stick of bombs wide of the airfield target.

# Fort Bridgewoods

The changeover of the wireless watch was just taking place and two troop transports had just arrived at Fort Bridgewoods to transport the ATS girls back to their quarters at Brompton Barracks. The transports were being driven by a member of the Women's Transport Service of the First Aid Nursing Yeomanry (FANY).

It was normal practice for the trucks to stop on the access trackway, but due to the air raids that that had been in progress one of the drivers brought her vehicle fully onto the drawbridge to afford protection to her passengers as they exited from the gate lodge.

A number of ATS teleprinter operators had already got into the vehicle as the single bomb scored a direct hit. Three ATS girls were killed, as was one of the EWAs. One of the FANY drivers, who had been extensively burnt as well as suffering numerous shrapnel wounds, died some time after being rushed to hospital.

**Cap badge of the First Aid Nursing Yeomanry Transport Service (FANY).**

One of the girls involved in the incident, ATS Sergeant Gladys Webb, had her hair burnt but returned to duty the following day. She was subsequently awarded a commendation for her courage. Some years later she was able to recall the night clearly. There had been no air raid warning and she recalled that the Sergeant of the Guard was just fixing the retaining clip on the tailboard of the lorry when there was a violent explosion. She recalled a male voice shouting very loudly 'jump', which she did. It had been one of the EWAs coming off duty and who had spotted that there was still someone alive in the back of the truck. Her hair was burnt and she had shrapnel wounds to her arm that were tended by a Royal Navy doctor who had arrived on the scene, probably from either Fort Borstal or more likely the Borstal Institution which was by now under naval control.

Section Commander Worster was about twenty feet away as the bomb exploded, and although he had been somewhat stunned by the explosion he managed to get himself to the blazing lorry and despite the risk to his own safety he approached the vehicle where the FANY driver was unconscious in the driving seat with her clothing well alight. Dragging her from the cab of the truck he beat out the flames with his bare hands and pulled her to safety. Not content with one rescue he then went back, accompanied by Mr R Hilder, an air-raid warden. Between them they rescued three more ATS girls from the blazing wreck of the lorry.

The EWA killed was Ernie Stagg. The bomb had fallen just feet away from the drawbridge and he had been killed outright by the blast as he passed through the gates from the entranceway tunnel, which can be seen in the photograph. The Sergeant of the Guard, who was from the Surrey Regiment, had one of his

**The bridge over the moat to the entrance of Fort Bridgewoods. It was here that the FANY transport was waiting when the bomb exploded.**

arms blown off. He also subsequently died of his wounds.

The second FANY driver, whose vehicle had been parked on the trackway leading to the drawbridge, had escaped unharmed.

Andrew Connolly, who had transferred to Fort Bridgewoods from the Royal Navy to work as an EWA, was one of those coming off duty at the time of the bomb incident. He had just exited from the gate lodge and crossed the drawbridge when he heard the unmistakable sound of the bomb falling and dived under one of the lorries; thankfully not the one that took the full force of the blast! Connolly may well have been the EWA who had shouted to Sergeant Webb, urging her to jump from the back of the burning lorry. If he was, he clearly saved her life.

As the raiding aircraft turned for their home airfields, the remainder of the off going shift were just leaving the Fort through the main gate, where they were met with the horrific scene as the fire brigade continued to hose down the remains of the wrecked vehicle with the bodies of the three dead ATS girls silhouetted against the night sky, still in their seated positions with their tin helmets covering their heads. Sadly their bodies were still too hot to be recovered.

Sid Wort, Lt Cdr Ellingworth's second in command at the station, had the grim task of attending the local hospital mortuary the following day, in order to properly identify the bodies.

Ironically an aerial photograph of Rochester Airport and the key installations had been taken by the German Air Force during the remaining months of peace in 1939.

**Aerial reconnaissance photograph taken by the German Air Force during the summer of 1939, prior to the outbreak of war. Forts Bridgewoods, Borstal, Horsted and Luton are visible, as is the Pobjoy works, Rochester Aerodrome and the Shorts Brothers factory. Interestingly the intelligence assessment does not identify Fort Bridgewoods as a potential target of military importance.**
**© German Air Force, Bundesarchiv.**

# Chapter 10. Ellingworth's secret

Lt Cdr Ellingworth was a man of secrets. He had been that way throughout the whole his working life, and when the time came for him to finally leave this world to meet the maker he worshipped he quietly expired with his secrets still intact.

On 6 of January 1940 Lt Cdr Ellingworth had been personally inducted into the greatest British secret of the war, Ultra, the Intelligence derived from the breaking by Bletchley Park of the German High-grade Enigma code. On this day he was told, in the most guarded of terms, that the primary German Air Force Key had been broken.

Ellingworth had always maintained tight control of operational security at Fort Bridgewoods and was consequently totally taken aback when, two days after his personal induction into the Ultra secret, and with the dire warnings given should he divulge its existence still fresh in his mind, one of his ATS teleprinter operators approached him with a service message that had just been teleprinted from Bletchley Park which read:

'Please repeat message ******, as we are waiting to decode it'

The ATS operator had clearly seen the significance of the message and had brought it immediately to the attention of her commanding officer and no one else.

Quite early on in the war, as was seen in the previous chapter, a system was brought in at Fort Bridgewoods which required them to send immediately the preamble and first groups to Bletchley Park over the direct teleprinter link. These became known at Chatham as 'Welchman Specials'. On one evening a telephone call was received by the supervisor at Chatham on the direct line from Bletchley Park to tell them to stop sending this traffic register for the time being. The supervisor, whilst taking the message, had been conscious of cheers and the like in the background and innocently asked if there was a party going on, only to be told 'Don't you know old boy, we've just broken RED' (the main German Air Force High-grade Enigma cypher). Thereafter every time the supervisor at Fort Bridgewoods received an instruction from Bletchley Park to stop the register, it was met by cheers around the interception station. Whilst clearly they should not have had even a hint of Bletchley Park having broken into the German Air Force high-grade code, they had clearly worked it out for themselves!

Ellingworth had another secret; one that he revealed during an overnight visit to Gordon Welchman in Hut 6 at Bletchley Park. Although Fort Bridgewoods had been closed down as the primary military wireless telegraphy interception station and reduced to a training establishment for EWAs, that was not the truth of it. He revealed that he maintained a small staff of EWAs at Bridgwoods, in order to have a diversity of interception; that is to say if Beaumanor could not hear it, Fort Bridgewoods might be better located due to the very nature of High Frequency radio propagation.

Following the move of the main military wireless interception operation from Fort Bridgewoods to Chicksands Priory and thereafter Beaumanor, there remained a great demand for additional trained interception operatives. The small training school established at Fort Bridgewoods was to provide civilian EWAs alongside the wealth of Royal Signals and ATS Special Wireless Operators (SWOPS).

Clearly the method of recruitment had to be such as not to reveal the secret nature of the work. In consequence Ellingworth had a cunning wheeze to trawl the Public, Grammar and Technical Schools in towns surrounding Rochester, where Fort Bridgwoods was located, with a view to gathering a crop of suitable young people who showed an aptitude for Morse code.

Ellingworth's own son John, who was a senior pupil at Kings School at Rochester, was one of the early recruits. Post war he was, like the other schoolboys, conscripted into the Royal Corps of Signals, in which he rose to the rank of Major. His final appointment was as officer commanding 224 Signal Squadron, who at that time were located on a site adjacent to Beaumanor. This Squadron had the task of training Royal Signals Special Operators.

Another schoolboy recruit was Cyril Norman Le Gassick (known as Sandy), whose

**The Upper Bell Public House, Chatham, with Sandy Le Gassick's father in the doorway. © KM Media Group.**

father had served as an officer in the Royal Artillery during the Great War, earning the Military Cross and Croix De Guerre. He, like many others, had suffered redundancy with the swinging of the Geddes Axe in 1923 and had instead taken command of the Upper Bell public house at the top of Bluebell Hill on the North Downs between Chatham and Maidstone, perhaps a mile or so from Fort Bridgewoods. The photograph of the pub was taken by a staff photographer from the *Kent Messenger* newspaper. When the author sent a copy to Sandy Le Gassick he was astounded, as the gentlemen stood in the doorway was none other than his own dear father.

# Fort Bridgewoods

**Sir Joseph Williamson Mathematical School in Rochester High Street, where Sandy Le Gassick attended school.** © *Chatham Observer*.

Sandy was a pupil at Sir Joseph Williamson Mathematical School in Rochester, and later at Maidstone Grammar School. Mr Adams, a quiet and mysterious customer who frequented the saloon bar of the Upper Bell later transpired to be a member of staff at Fort Bridgewoods, where he was involved in administrative work as second in command. When he enquired what Sandy intended to do on leaving school, it was indicated that he would probably follow in his father's footsteps and join the army. Sandy had already been economic with the truth about his age, to join the Home Guard where he had already risen to the rank of Company Sergeant Major in 'C' Company, 13 (Kent) Battalion, Home Guard.

Mr Adams made Sandy an offer of an appointment in the War Office which was subject to his passing an aptitude test. The offer was accepted with interest and Sandy, along with a group of young men of school leaving age, attended Fort Bridgewoods. It was only some three miles from his home, on the road to Rochester. Sandy had often passed the Fort in his travels to Rochester and had noticed that it had two large wireless masts, with a number of long wire aerials strung between them. Like all schoolboys of the era, Sandy had an interest in the magic that was the physics of radio.

The aptitude test was to determine the ability to learn the Morse code, and having successfully passed the test he joined other school leavers who had been selected in learning Morse to a standard of 22 words a minute. A number of the potential recruits had failed the aptitude test and others who were selected could not progress beyond the plateau of 5 words per minute. At the end of the intensive training a total of 38 young men were passed out and deemed ready for operational duty.

The training took place between the hours of 09:00 and 17:00, Monday to Saturday, and there were frequently tests to assess progress. Their instructors were Les Hadler, Mr Boyak, and their

**Maidstone Grammar School 1st XI in 1941. Sandy Le Gassick is standing on the far left back row. Friend and later fellow EWA Aubrey Stevens is seated on the far left front row.** © **Lt Col Le Gassick MBE, Royal Signals Rtd.**

senior instructor Albert Stevens. The training officer was Mr William 'Pop' Blundell, a retired Royal Signals Warrant Officer.

After six weeks of intensive training the new recruits moved to the main set room. They were placed under the supervision of one of the EWAs, who would then take over their tuition and induct them into the mysteries of operating signals and all the other tricks of the German operators. Some of those operators are recalled as being; Bob Roberts, Ollie Pearce, Harry Dix, Eric Millhouse, Alec Keenlyside, Ron Smith, Jerry Dalton, Fred Fox and Ken Oak. The recruits thereafter worked alongside their EWA mentors and kept the same routine watches of 06:00 to 14:00, 14:00 to 22:00 and 22:00 to 06:00 hrs.

**Bertram Ashman, Experimental Wireless Assistant trained at Fort Bridgewoods.**
**© Bertram Ashman.**

Recruited at the same time as John Ellingworth and Sandy Le Gassick was Bertram Ashman, seen in the photograph **left**, who was becoming bored with his clerical job working at Springfield Library in Maidstone. Working nearby as a clerical assistant in the Education Office was Aubrey Stevens, who had attended Maidstone Grammar School, along with Bertram Ashman and Sandy Le Gassick. Aubrey's father, Albert Edward Stevens, was a retired Royal Navy Chief Petty Officer Telegraphist and had worked for a time at Chicksands Priory, before being appointed an instructor at Fort Bridgewoods. His Morse was impeccable and he would comfortably read the code at 28 words per minute. From 1943 until 1945 he was the Chief Instructor at Fort Bridgewoods, teaching the new teenage intakes, but also worked with Mr Adams in his recruiting efforts.

In the 1920's Stevens was serving in Hong Kong as a Petty Officer Telegraphist. He was subsequently rated as a Chief Petty Officer Telegraphist. Following a subsequent draft to HMS Cardiff he was invalided out of the Royal Navy, having contracted Tuberculosis. This was diagnosed as having been contracted as a result of his earlier service in submarines. Perhaps an interesting aside from his time in submarines – and the author has been privileged to see copies of the official documents – was a proposal made by Petty Officer Stevens to Their Lordships of the Admiralty for the use of a trailing wire aerial that could be used by submarines to receive wireless telegraphy traffic whilst submerged. Flag Officer Submarines wrote a warm reply to Stevens, thanking him for his idea, but it was not pursued as the naval constructors could not see a way of feeding the wire safely through the pressure hull of a submarine. Inter-

**Petty Officer Albert Stevens, whilst serving in Hong Kong.**
**© Aubrey Stevens.**

# Fort Bridgewoods

estingly modern hunter killer submarines and the 'Bombers' have used a trailing wire aerial to receive VLF signals whilst submerged, a retrospective tribute to the foresight of Albert Stevens RN.

Anecdotal evidence provided to the author by Aubrey Stevens, from a post-war conversation with his father, provides an insight into a crucial period of the war when the hunt for the German battleship Bismarck was an absolute priority for the Royal Navy, who needed to carry out the Prime Minister's directive 'Sink the Bismarck', following the catastrophic loss of HMS Hood.

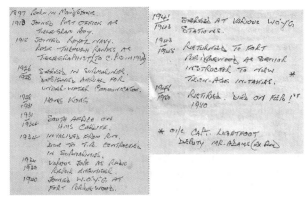

**Albert Stevens' career, recorded by his own hand. © Aubrey Stevens.**

Albert Stevens had received a summons to the office of his commanding officer, Lt Cdr Ellingworth Royal Navy Rtd, and naturally thought the worst as Ellingworth was not the type who would call you in just to pass the time of day or discuss the state of the weather.

Instead of the expected 'rollocking' he was invited to take a seat and handed a large glass of whisky. 'Congratulations' said Ellingworth, 'the long Morse message that you intercepted the other day was the only copy that Bletchley Park were able to decipher, in fact your efforts helped to sink the Bismarck'. Whilst the words are clearly a son's recollection of a conversation with his father, the fact is that this must stand as a real tribute to the former Chief Petty Officer Telegraphist, whose Morse was always impeccable. One can almost imagine the scene, two middle aged retired sailors sharing a glass of fine whisky whilst with sadness reflecting on the loss of the 'Mighty Hood', pride of the British Royal Navy, yet sharing in the knowledge that they, and in particular Mr Stevens, had played an all-important part in the destruction of one of Hitler's most dangerous naval assets.

**The German Battleship Bismarck: © Kriegmarine, Bundesarchiv.**

In the meantime Sandy Le Gassick, along with the other newly qualified EWAs, were sent to Beaumanor Hall and went on shift in Hut 'H', with all the other civilian EWAs. This was the new Fort Bridgewoods.

Sandy Le Gassick subsequently joined with Aubrey Stevens and Phillip Cooper to man HF and MF direction finding stations at Newton Morrell in North Yorkshire.

Sandy, like John Ellingworth, went on to serve post 1945 with the Royal Signals, retiring in 1980 in the rank of Lieutenant Colonel. He was appointed to the order of Member of the British Empire in 1967.

Many years after his war service Sandy received one last honour, that of a pin badge and certificate, issued by the Veterans Agency in recognition of the part that he played in the breaking of the Enigma Code. The presentation was made to Sandy by his local Member of Parliament, Sir Malcolm Bruce.

The DF station at Newton Morrell. Sandy Le Gassick is stood left, with supervisor Wally Ratcliffe centre. Aubrey Stevens is standing right. The photograph was taken by the third operator, Philip Cooper.
© Lt Col Le Gassick MBE, Royal Signals Rtd.

Yet another of the young men to arrive for training at Fort Bridgewoods was Chris Barnes. He had not been one of the schoolboys that had been recruited from Chatham, Rochester, Maidstone and Sutton Valance in that same year (1942). He was already in employment, working for Kent Education Committee at their offices in Sittingbourne. Whilst working at the office one day he came across a notice of a trawl for grammar school leavers to apply for interview at Fort Bridgewoods. Applicants had to be aged seventeen years and over.

**Lt C N Sandy Le Gassick, receiving his pin badge and certificate from Sir Malcolm Bruce MP, in recognition of his part in breaking the Enigma code.**
© *The Press and Journal*, Aberdeen

Chris Barnes made his application and was in time interviewed by a Captain Lightfoot. He passed the interview and the aptitude tests, and commenced training almost immediately. He subsequently found out that Captain Lightfoot was the officer in charge at Fort Bridgewoods and his deputy was Mr Adams. Barnes was to recall that his instructors were Boyak and Stevens, the latter being the senior instructor. The training regime was tightly focused, with endless sessions of Morse code and lessons in radio procedure (Q Code) and radio terminology. He became very proficient at reading Morse code, but no training was ever given in wireless telegraphy, that is the art of sending the Morse code, as the work to be conducted required them to be 'silent operators'. None of the trainees were given any real insight as to the actual work that they would be undertaking and he left the Fort, like many others, with little idea of what he had been trained to do. This perhaps reflects the level of security that surrounded the wireless interception organization and ultimately the Ultra secret.

In 1945 a party of EWAs mustered in the courtyard at Beaumanor, in order for Howard Jellings to be able to take a photograph of the Home Guard which was made up almost entirely of the young men that Ellingworth had recruited from Kent schools. As a backdrop was 'Cornwallis', who had previously watched over the EWAs as they came

# Fort Bridgewoods

and went at Fort Bridgewoods. As civilians they had to carry out some form of uniformed war work and theirs was the Home Guard, as had been the case at Fort Bridgewoods. In the centre at the front can be seen Lt Cdr Ellingworth, although dressed in the uniform of a Lieutenant Colonel, a rank he had been appointed to by the War Office. It is suspected that it was too much for the Army to have a Royal Navy Officer, albeit retired, at the head of their most primary interception station. Anecdotal evidence suggests that Ellingworth had the last laugh, as he hoisted a battle sized White Ensign over his station at Beaumanor on VE Day!

The only lady in the photograph was Ellingworth's daughter Margaret, who by this time had been employed in a clerical appointment.

These young men became known as the 'Gallant 78', as despite assurances that their vital war work as EWAs would count as military service they all went on to be conscripted into the army once the war ended.

*BEAUMANOR HOME GUARD, 21 PLATOON, 10TH (CHARNWOOD) BATTALION, LEICESTER HG*

**The Beaumanor Home Guard, made up almost entirely of the Kent schoolboys recruited and trained at Fort Bridgewoods.**
**© Howard Jellings.**

The senior instructor at Fort Bridgewoods was William Blundell, known affectionately as 'Pop'. He had been born on 13 July 1888 in Northamptonshire and sadly his parents both died whilst he was very young. He was subsequently raised by various aunts and uncles, some of whom were of the Quaker faith. He attended school until the age of eight, although after this his life is a bit of a mystery until he volunteers to join the army at the tender age of fifteen. He had lied to the recruiting Sergeant, telling him he was seventeen, and his actual age was to remain somewhat of an enigma until it finally appeared on his death certificate.

Upon joining the army, and following basic training, he was posted to India where he had the good fortune that one of his officers arranged for him to attend school, where he did well and gained his school certificate. Having now completed his education he was of far more use to the army and started work as a dispatch rider. Subsequently he was selected to train in the most up-to-date system of military signaling, wireless telegraphy.

In 1921 he had returned from India and presented himself at his brother's house in Northampton. It was here he was to meet his future wife, Mary Winifred, who lived just a couple of streets away. Upon returning to India he took with him his fiancé. They were married in St John's Church at Colaba, which was a suburb of Bombay. Interestingly, the house in Haig Avenue, Rochester where the family was living whilst he was working at Fort Bridgewoods, was named Colaba.

**St Johns Church, Mumbai. © Diocese of Mumbai.**

# Ellingworth's secret

By this time William Blundell had been transferred to the Royal Corps of Signals, newly formed from its origins with the Corps of Royal Engineers. By the time of his retirement from the army he had risen to the rank of Warrant Officer Second Class.

William 'Pop' Blundell was one of the five who opened the wireless interception station at Fort Bridgewoods in 1926 and had been one of the bearers when they buried their first commanding officer in 1934. He was a 'hardcore' EWA and Ellingworth fully recognised his ability and talents.

**'Pop' Blundell and his wife Mary, taken whilst on a pre-war boat trip to Southend on Sea.**
© **Cynthia Adams.**

When Fort Bridgewoods finally closed he moved to the main wireless interception station at Beaumanor and continued to work as an EWA, until he retired in 1953, the same year as Lt Cdr Ellingworth.

'Pop' Blundell was tragically widowed in 1946, when his wife Mary was killed in a road traffic accident outside the White Horse Public House on Chatham Hill. She had just got off of a bus and sadly, whilst attempting to cross from behind the bus, was hit by another bus that pulled round the stationary one. The investigation into the death found it to be a tragic accident and the driver was allowed to continue his driving career. This had even wider and more tragic consequences than anyone in 1946 could ever imagine.

On the evening of Tuesday 4 December 1951, 57-year-old driver John Sampson of the Maidstone and District Bus Company was driving a double decker bus down Dock Road in Chatham. The only illumination on the vehicle was sidelights, which tragically was the normal practice at this time. Marching ahead of him were 52 Royal Marine Cadets, all aged under 18 years. They were on their way to the Royal Naval barracks, for a boxing match. The cadets never reached the gates of HMS Pembroke, just some 200 yards away, for Driver Sampson ploughed into the squad of cadets killing 24 of them.

Driver Samson had 40 years experience as a driver, both on trams and then buses, and was due to receive a long service medal from his employer the Maidstone and District Bus Company.

John Samson appeared for trial at the Old Bailey, charged with the deaths of the 24 young cadets by careless driving. He was found guilty, but the jury made a plea to the judge for leniency on the basis of the mental suffering already experienced by Samson since the night

**Scene of the accident in Dock Road, Chatham, the morning after a party of Marine Cadets were killed and injured when they were run down by a bus.**
© *Chatham Observer*.

The bus driven by John Samson **on the evening he ploughed into a squad of marching Marine Cadets in Dock Road, Chatham.**
Credit: *Chatham Observer*.

of the accident. He was indeed given a lenient sentence, a £20 fine and a three year ban from driving.

From newspaper articles of the time it has been established that when the accident had been reported to the sailors on duty at the gate of HMS Pembroke, many had been released to offer whatever help they could. What they found upon their arrival at the scene was carnage and many were in tears as they gave first aid to the survivors and did what they could for the dead.

The funeral of the Cadets took place in Wood-lands Cemetery, Gillingham. They were afforded full military honours. The bodies of the Cadets had lain in the church the night before, with Royal Marines providing an honour guard for each.

**Funeral of the Marine Cadets killed in the bus tragedy at Chatham. The coffins were carried by Royal Marines from the Barracks at Chatham.**
© *Chatham Observer.*

Following the death of his wife, his retirement from Beaumanor and 'Y' work, 'Pop' Blundell disappeared from the home he lived in with his daughter and her husband. It was the last time Cynthia was to see her father and she remained unaware that he had found his new home in the Royal Hospital at Chelsea. He passed away at the age of 73 and is buried with many other proud Chelsea Pensioners in the Military Cemetery in Woking.

**'Pop' Blundell's daughter Cynthia, now long a widow herself, at her father's graveside for the first time, having made her peace with him.**
© **Cynthia Adams.**

Peter James, who trained as an EWA at Fort Bridgewoods, particularly recalled that 'Pop' Blundell had a beautiful daughter, but the young EWAs could not get near her – because 'Pop' wouldn't let them! He also recalled Mr Adams, the shadowy figure who frequented the saloon bar of the Upper Bell pub and recruited the landlord's son, Sandy Le Gassick. Adams was also a retired Royal Navy Chief Petty Officer telegraphist who had served in the fleet air arm. When in a chatty mood, Adams had some very interesting tales to tell!

The author had the privilege of interviewing Cynthia, 'Pop's' beautiful daughter. She was so proud that her son John had been trained in the Morse code by 'Pop' when he was studying for the amateur radio examination and licence. John now holds the amateur radio callsign G3ZSE. Neither John nor his sister Sue were aware of the full extent of their grandfather's involvement in the secret wireless war.

Lt Cdr Ellingworth's plan to recruit schoolboys was supported from a very strange quarter, The Church. Ellingworth and his wife were very religious in their beliefs and he was a Church Warden at

St Mary's Church in Strood. The vicar of St Mary's, the Reverend Donald L Brand, was recruited by Ellingworth to make recommendations of suitable young men for recruitment for secret war work. He also provided accommodation at the Vicarage for those recruited from the more distant schools in Kent. Brand had served in the Royal Navy during the Great War and one wonders if this was the link between the two. During the run-up to war the Ellingworth family were living in Watts Avenue, Rochester which has, at the end of the road, a fine church where one of Nelson's Captains at Trafalgar is buried. It does make one wonder why the family would travel some three or more miles to church when they had a perfectly good one, with a significant interest for any naval officer, so close to their home.

Whilst not connected directly to the Fort Bridgewoods story it is perhaps interesting to view the full photograph of the wedding that took place at Beaumanor, because it has an interesting story attached to it that involves the proclivities of Lt Cdr Ellingworth. The photograph was taken at the wedding of Fred Staddon, an EWA, to Kay Metcalf of the ATS, in the church at Barrow on Soar and was presided over by the Rev Donald Brand the Vicar of St Mary's, Strood. Brand can be clearly seen at the far right of the photograph. Ellingworth can be seen standing far left with the Bride's widowed mother

The wedding that took place at Beaumanor. Rev. Donald L Brand, who helped Ellingworth recruit young men to train and work as EWA's at Fort Bridgewoods, is on the extreme right. © Kay Staddon.

next to him. What was unusual about this occasion was that Ellingworth was there at all. He often received invitations to such events and it was normal for him to politely decline. On this occasion he had not responded but it was assumed that, as on other such occasions, he was not going to attend. To the surprise of both bride and groom Ellingworth arrived dressed as in full army uniform. As he was unaccompanied, and the Bride's mother was a widow, he immediately did the gentlemanly thing and spent the rest of the day as the lady's escort!

In a strange twist brought about by the necessity of war, the Vicar of St Mary's and Lt Cdr Ellingworth had become true 'fishers of men'.

Bert Taylor, who had till the early years of war been a pupil at Kings School in Rochester, recalled that he responded in early 1943 to an advertisement for young men to do important war work and that he was required to travel to Beaumanor for interview. Bert was able to tell the author that his interview was conducted – although he did not realise it at the time – by Colonel Ellingworth. During the interview he was asked if he knew a John Ellingworth and, as it transpired, Bert had sat next to him in classes at Kings and was able to say so. Bert, to this day, retains the impression that his positive response eased his entry into the secret world of wireless interception.

Upon his acceptance for training Bert was required to present himself to Fort Bridgewoods, where his initial training was in the Morse code. He recalls two instructors,

# Fort Bridgewoods

one Albert Stevens and the other, whose name time has wiped from his memory, was a retired Royal Navy submariner who had been involved in an incident where he had been gassed when sea-water had interacted with his submarine's batteries. As a result of this he spoke with a very hoarse voice.

Once Bert's Morse proficiency was to the required standard he was transferred into the main set room at Fort Bridgewoods, where he worked on live groups under the direct supervision of one of the experienced EWAs. From a record made at the time Bert was able to recall that on 3 May 1943 from 07:02 hrs until 12:16 hrs he was covering a group transmitting on 5240kHz and that his operating position was set F1.

One final recollection that Bert held was in respect of the aerial masts at Fort Bridgewoods, having on one occasion started to climb one but, but when he reached a height of about 20ft discretion became the better part of valour and he came back down. To the best of his recollection the aerials ran NW to SE, with the masts seated on the chalk bank.

One common recollection of all the schoolboys who trained as EWAs at Fort Bridgewoods was the endless grind of Morse code training, with those who did not progress beyond the watershed of five words per minute being quickly weeded out and shepherded back out of the gates of the fort with dire warnings about the penalties for breaking the Official Secrets Act which all had signed upon arrival for training. At the end of each week the Chief Instructor Albert Stevens would appear in the training classroom and administer a test of their skill and competence in taking down his impeccable Morse.

Interestingly a number of the schoolboys recalled the training room, with its long wooden table, complete with Morse key and training oscillator. Whilst conducting local research the author had occasion to have a conversation with a local Scout leader, Ray 'Doc' Ingle, whose father had been an officer at Rochester Borstal during the war years. The family had lived in a married quarter in Sir Evelyn Road. Ray recalled that as a young boy during the war period he and some friends had climbed into Fort Bridgewoods via the moat, believing the fort to be abandoned. He recalled entering one of the underground rooms, which was furnished with a long wooden table with a Morse key. It was at this point they noticed that there was a clock on the wall which was ticking and keeping the right time. In the realisation that the fort was indeed occupied they fled, expecting at any moment to be shot as spies!

# Chapter 11. Ellingworth

On 15 December 1889 in Oakham, Rutland a boy was born to Henry and Nellie Ellingworth (nee Marshall). The boy was named Marshall John William Ellingworth and he was destined to play a significant role in naval and military communications in both the first and second World Wars, and into the Cold War era.

Marshall had a sister, Dolce, and brothers, Frank and Harry. They grew up in the family home above the business at 14 Melton Road, Oakham. The family were photographers and had their studio in the garden at the rear of the shop. They were also musicians, billposters and town criers! Henry Ellingworth passed away unexpectedly in 1907, at the young age of 47.

**Henry Ellingworth.**
**© Malcolm Ellingworth.**

Henry Ellingworth's first wife Emma had died in 1988 from kidney failure and he remarried in the following year to Eleanor Marshall (known as Nellie). Harry Ellingworth took control of the family business in 1910. Both Harry and Frank served in the army during the Great War.

Harry Ellingworth served in the 1st Battalion of the Rutland Volunteer Regiment. Frank Ellingworth had joined the Leicestershire Regi-

**Marshall's mother Nellie and sister Dolce, standing outside the family business and home in around 1918. Marshall's bedroom window can be seen above the main shop-front sign. © Malcolm Ellingworth.**

# Fort Bridgewoods

ment of the Territorial Army in 1911 as a bandsman [number 8028]. There is anecdotal evidence that he may have served during the Great War in the Royal Flying Corps, but as yet this has not been corroborated. Frank Ellingworth went on to be a professional cellist and continued as a musician for sixteen years, before taking up employment with the Electricity Board.

Taken around 1910-11, George Ellingworth (uncle) with his arms in a formal folded pose, Francis (Frank) Ellingworth, Nellie Ellingworth (Mother), Harry Ellingworth, Marshall Ellingworth and Dinah (whose mother Emma Chamberlain had been Henry's first wife). © Malcolm Ellingworth.

In 1948 Cdr Ellingworth was interviewed for the *Beaumanor Staff Magazine* by Ralph Champion who was in civilian life a professional journalist, working freelance for the *Daily Express* and post war as the New York correspondent for the *Daily Mirror*. At the very start of the article it noted that on the wall of Cdr Ellingworth's office was an official notice, part of which ran "1899 – No mention has been made of the Marconi System which has tremendous possibilities but seems a long way off being tried yet". At the time that this was first written Cdr Ellingworth was just 10 years old and useable wireless was still almost a decade away.

**Oakham School.**

The young Marshall Ellingworth won a scholarship to attend Oakham School and on one occasion was taunted by his fellow public school boys for being the son of a 'tradesman'. This caused him to run away, making his way to his uncle William's house in Leicester with nothing more than a postage stamp in his pocket.

Upon leaving school Marshall Ellingworth joined the Royal Navy at HMS Ganges on 18 May 1906 as a boy second class, at the age of 15. On 30 November 1906 he was rated boy first class and on the 15 December 1907, his sixteenth birthday, he signed on for twelve years service.

In 1909 the young Marshall Ellingworth was selected for training in the new Telegraphist Branch and took the first step in his life-long relationship with wireless communications. One of his first jobs as a telegraphist was to go aloft, shinning up a 220ft high

**Marshall Ellingworth in 1907, whilst on leave, dressed in his Sunday best in the garden of 14 Melton Road, Oakham. The photograph was taken by his brother Harry. © Malcolm Ellingworth.**

mast of a battleship and **square** the wireless aerial. The radio equipment on the ship was primitive. Part of it consisted of a Coherer, a sealed glass tube filled with iron filings which theoretically produced wireless signals on a tape and also rang a bell. From Ellingworth's later recollection this device performed so efficiently that every time there were atmospherics the bell clanged and the operator had to rush from the deck, his bunk, or wherever he happened to be. He also recalled that on the Coherer was a notice 'do not thump'; although the temptation was irresistible at times. Only in 1910 was voice communication introduced into the Royal Navy.

HMS Cressy. The tall fore and main masts still carried the fighting platforms from which the ship's guns were directed. The wireless aerials were rigged between them. © MoD 2014.

**Marshall Ellingworth as a naval rating. Photo taken prior to the Great War, possibly after 1912, as he has a medal ribbon which is likely to be the King George V Coronation Medal. The lady in the photograph is his mother, Nellie. © Malcolm Ellingworth.**

Ellignworth joined his first ship, HMS Cressy, on 17 September 1907. It is perhaps interesting to note that in September 1914 HMS Cressy was one of three light cruisers operating off the Coast of Holland. All three were of obsolete type and had until recently been part of the reserve fleet at Chatham. Had it not been for the outbreak of war these ships would have been destined for the breakers yard. This was the 'Live Bait Squadron' and bait they certainly were, for they were spotted by the captain of a German submarine, U9, which was on patrol in the area. Within the hour all three had been sunk, with great loss of life.

From 6 January 1908 until 19 June 1908 Marshall Ellingworth was posted to Pembroke Barracks, Chatham. From 20 June 1908 until 12 September 1908 he was on the ship's book for HMS Dominion and from 13 September 1908 until 12 October 1908 on the ship's book of HMS Black Prince. From 13 October he is found back on the ship's book of HMS Dominion, for what appears to be a full commission, during which he was rated Leading Telegraphist.

**HMS Black Prince. © MoD 2014.**

**HMS Dominion. © MoD 2014.**

# Fort Bridgewoods

Marshall Ellingworth was also an accomplished musician, playing both flute and violin. Whilst on leave from the navy he would often play as part of the Harry Ellingworth Quadrille Band.

Leading Telegraphist Ellingworth was not one to stand still and he quickly progressed to Petty Officer Telegraphist and then Chief Petty Officer Telegraphist. Shortly after the outbreak of the Great War Ellingworth was one of the youngest Chief Petty Officer Telegraphists in the fleet and responsible for the radio service of a flotilla of sixteen destroyers. Whilst in later life Ellingworth was not one to talk of his war service he was wounded in action on 28 April 1915. HMS Wolverine is recorded as an Ellingworth ship on his record of service but it is likely that this was one of the sixteen destroyers that he was responsible for. Whilst at action stations in the wireless office of Wolverine a shell hit the bridge above, killing the Captain, Officer of the Watch and the Coxswain. A tuner, which weighed about 40 pounds, fell and struck Chief Petty Officer Ellingworth on the head, injuring him so badly that he was to carry the scars for the rest of his life. Despite his injury Chief Petty Officer

**Marshall Ellingworth playing the flute, while brothers Harry and Frank are playing the double bass and cello respectively.**
© Malcolm Ellingworth.

Ellingworth remained at this post until the end of the action, for which he was to be awarded the Distinguished Service Medal (DSM).

Anecdotal evidence provided by Malcolm Ellingworth, a nephew, indicates that whilst HMS Wolverine was moored at Lemnos in the Dardanelles, a very distant cousin from Australia came aboard to meet Chief Petty Officer Ellingworth. This was Clifford

**HMS Wolverine at speed.**
© MoD 2014.

Ellingworth, a medic. An extract from Clifford Ellingworth's diary records "Two destroyers alongside. Still in harbour at Lemnos. Lovely morning. All ready to leave. Destroyer Wolverine. Just as I stepped on board I met Marshall Ellingworth, the wireless operator.

Great excitement. Had dinner and tea with him. Travelled very quickly and soon arrived at the famous hill where Australians first landed, came ashore in platoons and climbed up to our positions. Firing going on all the time, bullets dropping all round us. We had to set to and dig holes in the side of the hill to shelter from shrapnel. Great fun. Went to sleep to the noise of bullets cracking".

**Clifford Ellingworth, second from the right, part of the Australian Army landed at the Dardanelles.**
© Malcolm Ellingworth.

One of Clifford Ellingworth's descendants is married to Admiral of the Fleet, Lord Louis Mountbatten's granddaughter. Lord Louis was also proud to be a Naval Communicator and maintained close links to the branch throughout his life.

Ellingworth was serving in HMS Blenheim when advanced to Chief Petty Officer Telegraphist. He was transferred to HMS Wolverine and served aboard from 11 June 1916 until 31 August 1916. He then transferred back to HMS Blenheim and continued aboard until 9 February 1917.

**HMS Blenheim. © MoD 2014.**

Chief Petty Officer Ellingworth's last ship as a senior rating was HMS Europa. Having progressed promptly and with significant merit as a rating, he was selected for commissioning as a naval officer. The last entry on his rating's record of service is made on 30 June 1917, when he leaves HMS Europa, destined for Britannia Naval College and commissioning.

**HMS Europa. © MoD 2014.**

The newly commissioned Lieutenant Ellingworth Royal Navy was one of the first wireless officers to be chosen from the lower deck.

In 1920 Ellingworth was helping with experiments which revolutionised anti-submarine warfare 20 years later. He joined HMS Antrim, which had been placed into reserve at the Nore (Chatham Command) in 1919, but had been refitted as a wireless and ASDIC trials ship.

**HMS Antrim. © MoD 2014.**

Aboard HMS Antrim the first ASDIC or U-Boat detector was tested in shallow coastal waters. The ASDIC tube was 5ft in diameter, stretching to the actual keel of the ship and requiring a whole watch of sailors to haul it up.

Upon completion of these trials in 1921 Ellingworth was to be appointed as officer-in-charge Horsea Island High Power Wire-

**The quarters of the Officer in Charge of Horsea Island WT station. The receiver room can be seen just beyond the house. © MoD 2014.**

**The office of the Officer in Charge at Horsea Island WT station, surrounded by various masts that supported the aerial system. © MoD 2014.**

# Fort Bridgewoods

less Station, near Portsmouth. Following the arrival of wireless telegraphy, Horsea Island became the first of three high-powered shore wireless stations for the Royal Navy in March 1909. The equipment was regularly updated and Horsea remained in operational use as a wireless telegraphy station until the 1960s.

In 1923 Ellingworth was appointed to Singapore, to modernise the RN wireless telegraphy station at Seletar. Other appointments followed, including as officer-in-charge of the RN wireless telegraphy station at Malta where he had his most unnerving experience, having to participate in a cocktail party which was held at the top of a 600ft radio mast.

**Lt Ellingworth and his wireless telegraphists at Seletar WT station in 1923. Ellingworth is seated third from the right, centre row.**
© Malcolm Ellingworth.

**Lt M J W Ellingworth DSM RN and Eleanor his bride, on their wedding day in 1920. The wedding took place at Oakham Church.**
© Paul Caton.

Lt Ellingworth became a married man on 10 April 1920m with his marriage to Eleanor. In 1921 their first daughter Joyce was born and 18 September 1926 saw the birth of their twins John and Margaret.

On 15 December 1934 Ellingworth swallowed the anchor, retiring from the Royal Navy as a Lieutenant Commander. Not one to allow the grass to grow under his feet, the newly retired Cdr Ellingworth was to start a new career two weeks later in January 1935 as the officer commanding Wireless Section – Eastern Command Signal Company at Fort Bridgewoods.

At this time the family were living in Watts Avenue, Rochester, which was just under a mile away from his new command on the Maidstone Road. Watts Avenue is a select area, well suited to a retired naval officer and his family, indeed *Kelly's Directory* for the period shows that the majority of the other residents were very senior Royal Navy surgeons who were appointed to the nearby Royal Navy hospital at Chatham, the lowest rank at the time being Surgeon Commander.

**Watts Avenue, Rochester, on a snowy day in the 1930s.**
© *Chatham Observer*.

Prior to 1941 the family moved just around the corner from their Watts Avenue address to another well appointed house at 29 South Avenue, Rochester, which, like the properties in Watts Avenue, was eminently suited to a retired naval officer and his family.

**Number 3 Watts Avenue, in 2007.**

Sadly, since the 1940s, the properties in South Avenue have suffered badly.

From summer 1935 until the summer of 1939 John Ellingworth was a pupil at the nearby King's School at Rochester.

Cdr Ellingworth was a churchgoer and a churchwarden at St Mary's Church,

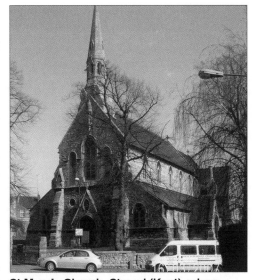

**Number 29 South Avenue. The condition of the property today does not properly reflect how these houses would have looked at the time the Ellingworths were resident there. South Avenue has since been renamed The Close.**

Strood. He was a good friend of the vicar, the Reverend Donald L Brand, who had served in the Royal Navy during the Great War. The Reverend Brand assisted Cdr Ellingworth by recruiting suitable young men for secret war work as Experimental Wireless Assistants at Fort Bridgewoods.

In 1941, as a result of casualties and damage caused by German bombers at Fort Bridgewoods, interception operations were transferred on a temporary basis to Chicksands, which was a site shared with the Royal Air Force. Whilst located here the organisation became known as Special Y Group or SYG. By 1942 there had been another move, this time to a permanent home at Beaumanor. Here his command was known as War Office Y Group [WOYG].

Lt Cdr Ellingworth was temporarily converted from RN to Army, when he was appointed as a Lieutenant Colonel in the Royal Signals, a rank he was to retain until the end of World War II. At the end of the war the Lt Col reverted to his old service rank of Lt Cdr and continued to command at

**St Mary's Church, Strood (Kent), where Ellingworth worshipped and was a Church Warden. Credit: Author's collection.**

# Fort Bridgewoods

Beaumanor until his retirement in 1953.

Whilst commanding at Beaumanor Lt Col Ellingworth and his wife made their home in an attractive cottage in Woodhouse village. The Ellingworths attended the Old Woodhouse Church and Redvers Webber recalls being 'intercepted' by him one Monday morning in a corridor at Beaumanor. "Your banns were read out yesterday morning in Old Woodhouse Church and you were not there", challenged the Colonel. Whilst at first stunned Redvers recovered his composure and replied "I was at my fiancée's church in Loughborough, Sir".

**Old Woodhouse Church St Mary in the Elms.**

During the war years at Beaumanor, the Ellingworth family lived at 231 Forest Road, Old Woodhouse. This is adjacent to The Holt, which was formerly the residence of the Vicar of Woodhouse. 231 Forest Road was also known as Butler's Cottage, as it was traditionally the home of the Head Butler to the Herrick family of Beaumanor Hall. It should be noted that the cottage had no garden, as butlers were not expected to get their hands dirty!

The sale catalogue for the Beaumanor Estate dated 1946 shows an entry for 231 Forest Road, Old Woodhouse, formerly known as 'Butler's Cottage', but now known just as 'The Cottage'. It also shows that at the time of the sale the tenant was Col Ellingworth.

By 1949 the Ellingworths were living in the Gatehouse Cottage, which is at the head of the main entrance driveway that leads up to Beaumanor Hall.

This is confirmed by an interesting little anecdote provided by Philip Blenkinsop, whose father was an EWA at Beaumanor. It would appear that Mr Blenkinsop had recruited a number of the family to the Y service and now it was the turn of Philip's uncle

**Butler's Cottage, now 'The Stables', Old Woodhouse, home to Lt Col Ellingworth and his family from 1942 to 1946.**

**Gatehouse Cottage, at the entrance to the driveway to Beaumanor Hall.**

Bob. It must have been Mr Blenkinsop's day off, as he was walking back up the drive following Bob's interview. As they approached the gate lodge, which formerly had a privet hedge rather than a low stone wall, Mr Blenkinsop announced "and this is where Trunky lives – he's a right *******" (inserting some mild but explicit remark which related to MJWEs legendary martinet qualities). As the remark had left Mr Blenkinsop's lips Lt Cdr Ellingworth's head appeared over the top of the hedge and greeted him with "lovely afternoon Mr Benkinsop". Mr Blenkinsop was convinced that Commander Ellingworth must have overheard his comment, but assumed that he had chosen to have the grace not to make an issue of it. Uncle Bob got the job!

In 1946 Commander Ellingworth was awarded an OBE for his war service. Upon retirement the Commander and his wife moved to the Southbourne area of Bournemouth, to be by the seaside and close to their eldest daughter.

**Nellie Ellingworth's 90th birthday. Those present are (L to R) sister Dolce, mother Nellie, brother Harry (at the rear), Commander Ellingworth and brother Frank. © Malcolm Ellingworth.**

Over the years the Ellingworth children married. Joyce Eleanor, the elder daughter, married Flying Officer Michael Francis Caton. Margaret Mary married Captain Thomas Hilliard Beaumont and John, his only son, was married in 1951.

The Commander and his wife settled into the house they had built in Sunnylands Avenue, Southbourne. They continued to be regular churchgoers and joined the congregation of St Katharine's Church, Southbourne, which was nearby. As at St Mary's, Strood, Commander Ellingworth served for many years as a churchwarden.

**St Katharine's Church, Southbourne, where Ellingworth and his wife worshiped in their retirement.**

Lt Commander Marshall John William Ellingworth DSM OBE passed away on 22 February 1976. Eleanor had passed away some years earlier. Anecdotal evidence provided by the family tells of his final days, when he was not able to cope well on his own. The family made the conscious and caring decision to make his final days as comfortable as they could in a well-appointed nursing home, but Ellingworth did not think very much of this – he quietly passed away on his first night at the home. There is no headstone in a quiet churchyard to find, as both he and his wife were cremated.

His only son, Major John Michael Elligworth MBE Royal Signals, became Mayor of Oakham, the family hometown, in 1984.

None of the children are living. Margaret passed away on 21 December 1998 and John in April 2000. Joyce, their elder daughter, passed away suddenly in November 2000.

# Fort Bridgewoods

Commander Ellingworth, in his day, had been at the very cutting edge of technology. He lived in a world of secrets and kept them all his life, perhaps why so little has been recorded of his contribution.

The Ellingworths have served their country well down the years. An Ellingworth served at Waterloo, although one suspects that Commander Ellingworth would have preferred it to have been at Trafalgar!

# Chapter 12.
# No-one cackled

Winston Churchill once described the staff at Bletchley Park as 'the geese that laid the golden eggs but never cackled', and one can be certain that this description was also directed at those of the 'Y' service who provided the very 'rabbits' from which the cryptographers made 'rabbit stew'.

Certainly until 1974 when F W Winterbotham published, without prior approval, his book *The Ultra Secret* there had been no leaks of the work carried out at Bletchley Park or by the 'Y' service. Winterbotham was the first to reveal the importance of the work carried out at Bletchley Park, where the high-grade German Enigma code had been broken following the interception of German wireless telegraphy traffic, although the process of interception was glossed over.

There are many notable anecdotes which have since appeared in various books, where wives have kept the secret of their Ultra-related war work from husbands and *vice versa*.

Probably the next most notable book was *Most Secret War*, by Professor R V Jones who, having spent his war as Assistant Direct of Intelligence (Science) at the Air Ministry, was able to reveal the importance of the decoded German Air Force wireless telegraphy signals in his battle against German technological advances, in particular the beam bombing system.

Gordon Welchman went further, identifying the vital part that the 'Y' service, and in particular Fort Bridgewoods under Lt Cdr Ellingworth, played in the breaking of the German high-grade Enigma code.

The Official Secrets Acts of 1911 and 1920, signed by all who were involved in the work at Bletchley Park and the 'Y' stations, was the very tool that was used to demand the silence of those who had done their part in what was after all the biggest British secret of World War II. Perhaps the only comparable secret of that war was the development of the atom bomb, although that was only to take months off the ending of the war with Japan. It is estimated that Ultra saved at least two years of bloodshed.

One has to ask why the secret was kept for so long. Perhaps Gordon Welchman hits the nail on the head when he identifies in his book, *The Hut Six Story*, that after the war the British Government sold captured Enigma machines to friendly allied powers, extolling their virtues and asserting that the product from them was unbreakable. Clearly GCHQ knew differently, and whilst they continued to be used by these friendly powers well into the 1960s the ability to read the traffic proved most useful in determining British Foreign Policy.

**KL7 (Adonis system) offline encryption machine. This machine is on display aboard HMS Belfast.**

Perhaps a second important reason was that the Allies, subsequently NATO, developed similar machines which, although far more electronically sophisticated, used the same principles. One in particular was in service for many years post war and was known as the ADONIS system or the KL7 offline encryption machine.

The ADONIS system also produced five letter groups, but this was printed out onto paper tape rather than using the field of lamps that was found on the top of the Enigma machine. The KL7 used a rotor system much in the same way as the Enigma machine, but far more rotors were employed, thus increasing many-fold the number of potential key settings. KL7 rotors have brass connections on each face and secret with this system, as with Enigma before it, was the way in which the rotors were wired between one face and the other.

Perhaps what is most important in the keeping of the secret of wireless interception is that the processes developed at Fort Bridgewoods were just as secret at the end of the war as they were before it started. It was only the target that had changed.

One intelligence officer, when inducting new intelligence officers to the secrets of signals intelligence during World War II, gave the dire warning that if any one of them ever revealed the secret of Ultra he would personally hunt them down and shoot them with his very own service revolver!

**Like Enigma machine rotors, KL7 (Adonis system) rotors were the key to its secret. © Cryptologic Museum.**

As the war with Germany drew to a close the EWAs of the new 'Chatham' just quietly retuned their sets and settled down to reading Russian Morse, rather than German. GC&CS turned into GCHQ and Beaumanor was just part of that bigger interception organisation. Many EWAs who thought that they had laid down their headphones were called back to service.

MY NIGHTMARE
BY WILK

A cartoon from the *Beaumanor Staff Magazine* depicts one such occasion when the 'nightmare' came true! Ellingworth is seen chaining the EWA to his set, by placing headphones on his head. He is wearing his three hats, Royal Navy, Army and civilian. © 'Wilk', *Beaumanour Staff Magazine*.

At the close of the War in Europe Ellingworth established his new course to the East. What followed, as they say, is just history!

For the EWAs it had never been a shooting war. They wore no uniform, and they certainly did they not come face to face with the enemy, yet every day the EWAs of Fort Bridgewoods had intercepted the innermost secrets of the enemy, albeit in what the Axis powers believed to be their unbreakable Enigma code.

Their war was one of secrets, the precise reading of Morse code often under very marginal atmospheric conditions; long shifts of listening to static, awaiting the enemy radio schedule and then second guessing the clever twists and turns of the enemy operators, as they applied their radio security techniques to avoid eavesdropping.

CARRY ON PULLING YOUR WEIGHT LADS , WHILE I SEE WHERE WE GO FROM HERE !

W.O.Y.G.

EUROPEAN WAR

The cartoon 'where do we go from here' appeared in a *Beaumanor Staff Magazine* in the closing weeks of World War II. It depicts a number of the EWAs in a service whaler, with Lt Cdr Ellingworth at the helm trying to work out just where they were to go from here. © 'Wilk', *Beaumanor Staff Magazine*.

Yet despite the long working hours, the endless rotation between night and day shifts, and the relentless pressure to make accurate Morse code interceptions, the EWAs of Fort Bridgewoods had achieved all that had been asked of them, and far more if the truth was to be known.

There were no special privileges, their rations were the same as any other civil-

# Fort Bridgewoods

ian and on top of their official war duties they still had to perform routine public duties as fire watchers, wardens or as members of the Home Guard.

There were few medals, indeed recognition of their war work was not marked in any real way until post Millennium, when those who had not already taken their secrets to the grave were finally recognised by the award of a special badge by the newly formed Veterans' Agency. It was scant reward for all they had achieved and the vital contribution they made to shortening the war in Europe, yet they wear them with great pride for a job well done.

And what of the schoolboys recruited from the schools of Kent and pressed into service at Fort Bridgewoods, Beaumanor and other secret listening outstations? Despite their contribution and certain assurances their dedicated war work did not exempt them from being called up, and as the war reached its close many like Sandy Le Gassick and John Ellingworth were called up and found themselves doing the self same work but now in uniform as members of the Royal Corps of Signals. Some gained commissions and enjoyed notable military careers doing just what their early training had prepared them for. Others completed their compulsory service and then found their way to GCHQ.

No matter what, theirs remained a world of constant vigilance, accurate interception of Morse code and latterly other complex modes of transmission, which provided the code breakers with the accurate signals products required to do their vital work. Yet over the years the one principal that has underpinned all of their work, and remains so even today, is one of extreme secrecy. Accordingly it has been a rare privilege to be able to pay this tribute to all of those who stood their watches within the walls of Fort Brigewoods and carved out the very foundations of the art and science of wireless interception and traffic analysis.

So as the world of Wireless Interception marched on, what had become of Fort Bridgewoods?

Anecdotal evidence suggests that at the close of 1945 Fort Bridgewoods had been placed into care and maintenance, being overseen by the Royal Engineers.

**A tangle of trees, bushes and long grass takes over the deep moat.**
© **Graham French.**

On occasions the fort was visited by parties of RE's as equipment was removed, but the radio equipment associated with wireless interception had been hurriedly removed before the end of the war and this was witnessed by the way in which wiring had been left hanging just as equipment had been ripped out.

Fort Bridgwoods started to grow back into obscurity, just as the grass and the hedgerow was starting to retake its natural place around the buildings and within the deep moat.

**The casemates at Fort Bridgewoods that once housed the set rooms where German Enigma code was taken are now silent, with nature taking over and vandals leaving them in a very sorry state. © Graham French.**

But Fort Bridgewoods had not yet passed from the thoughts of the War Office and as the Cold War started to get colder still and the British Government prepared for a Warsaw Pact nuclear first strike, a new lease of life was given to the old Victorian fort. In 1953 workmen arrived and in the secrecy afforded by the high grass banks and deep moat they set to work building a secret bunker, or Anti Air Operations Room (AAOR), on the parade ground facing the forts casemates. From this bunker was to be afforded the co-ordination of fixed anti aircraft weapon sites which had been established for the protection of Chatham Dockyard, Medway and the approach to London.

During the 1950s Great Britain's independent nuclear deterrent was provided by the Royal Air Force and the 'V' bomber force. America and the Warsaw Pact likewise still relied upon long range bombers to deliver strategic nuclear weapons. The Royal Observer Corps remained a vital part of the UK command and control system and Fort Bridgewoods was a vital cog in the nation's defence, albeit far too little when faced with a nuclear first strike. The AAOR remained operational until 1957.

Fort Bridgewoods passed into Home Office control in 1961 and the AAOR, now designated SRC 5.2, became a Sub Regional Control Centre for the administration of the South East

**External view of the AAOR bunker that was built into the parade ground of Fort Bridgewoods.
© Subterannia Britannica Collection.**

**The operations room of the AAOR bunker at Fort Bridgewoods, laid out very much like the RAF operations rooms of the Battle of Britain era. It had a viewing gallery for the senior officers, who would command the battle, and a plotting floor where the movement of enemy and friendly aircraft would be plotted on a map table.
© Subterrania Britannica Collection.**

# Fort Bridgewoods

London area in the event of a nuclear first strike. It was retained in that role until 1967.

Around this time the whole strategy for the delivery of nuclear weapons was being reviewed, with the bomber force being stood down in favour of a nuclear submarine bomber fleet that could stay at sea for months at a time and deliver intercontinental ballistic missiles from the hidden depths of the world's oceans. In Great Britain the baton was handed from the Royal Air Force to the Royal Navy. Similar strategic changes took place in the United States and within the Warsaw Pact.

Now, with only four minutes or less warning, the need to track bombers from a series of local control and co-ordination bunkers was obsolete, so by 1968 cuts followed in the Civil Defence budget and Fort Bridgewoods was finally declared redundant. Apart from curious schoolboys, history enthusiasts, those interested in the secret places of the Cold War era and – sadly – vandals, Fort Bridgewoods was left to quietly grow old with the grounds returning to nature.

**The Fort's gate lodge now standing alone, with the ditch filled-in and the earth banking and upper works gone. This is how Dr Philip Blenkinsop found it when he visited in about 1988. He intended to return to take more photographs, but when he did it was no longer there. © Dr Philip Blenkinsop.**

In the early 1970s the site was sold to Leggetts, a local property development company and in preparation for future development the moat was filled in.

In 1982 vandals entered the AAOR bunker and set a fire which caused considerable damage to the internal structure.

During this time plans were being drawn up to redevelop the site and these were put before Medway Council who, despite the Fort being a listed structure of major historic importance, gave approval for its final demolition and redevelopment.

Today there is nothing left of Fort Bridgewoods. The site is now a trading estate, but anecdotal evidence suggests that the underground structures were only filled in, as was the moat. The trading estate is certainly built on a series of concrete rafts which were laid over the site.

With the passing of time there is every chance that some latter-day 'Time Team' will rediscover what, at one time, was one of the most secret locations in the realm.

**Fort Bridgewoods Trading Estate now stands on the site of the old Victorian fort.**

# Bibliography

Sir Evelyn Ruggles-Brise KCB *The English Prison System* (Macmillan, 1921)

K R Gulvin *The Medway Forts*
(Medway Historical Ordnance, 2007)

Victor Smith *Front Line Kent* (Kent County Council, 2003)

John Ferris *The British Army and Signals Intelligence During the First World War* (Alan Sutton Publishing Ltd, 1992)

Peter Wright *Spycatcher* (Heinemann Australia, 1985)

Robin Denniston *Thirty Secret Years - A G Denniston's work in signals intelligence 1914-1944* (Cromwell Press, 2007)

R V Jones *Most Secret War* (Hamish Hamilton, 1978)

F W Winterbotham *The Ultra Secret* (Weidenfeld & Nicholson, 1974)

Basil Collier *Hidden Weapons Allied Secret or Undercover Services in World War II* (Hamish Hamilton, 1982)

Peter Calvocoressi *Top Secret Ultra* (Cassell Ltd, 1980)

F W Hinsley & Alan Stripp *Code Breakers - The Inside Story of Bletchley Park* (Oxford University Press, 1993)

Nigel West *GCHQ The Secret Wireless War 1900-86* (Weidenfeld & Nicholson, 1986)

Gordon Welchman *The Hut Six Story* (M & M Baldwin, 1997)

Robin J Brooks *Kent Airfields in the Second World War* (Countryside Books, 1998)

Len C Moore *Z17 My War Memories 1939-1945* (Len C Moore, 1996)

Joan Nicholls *England Needs You - The Story of Beaumanor Y Station, World War Two* (Joan Nicholls, 2000)

Hugh Skillen *Spies of the Airwaves* (Hugh Skillen, 1989)

Hugh Skillen *BSM Four Years of War-Time Wit and Humour in the Royal Signals/ATS/Intelligence Corps* (Hugh Skillen 1993)

# Fort Bridgewoods

Geoffrey Pidgeon    *The Secret Wireless War* (Geoffrey Pidgeon, 2003)

M J W Ellingworth    *The History of War Officer Y Group 1926-1945*
War Office 1948 (in 1948 classified TOP SECRET ULTRA)

Alfred Price    *Instruments of Darkness The History of Electronic Warfare, 1939-1945* (Harper Collins, 1979)

Pat Hawker    *Harold Kenworthy OBE - His Key Role in Signals Intelligence* (OTNews No. 61, Winer 2002)

Pat Hawker    *The Mysterious A J Alan – Leslie Harrison Lambert G2ST* (Radio Bygones, 1991)

John Pether    *Funkers and Sparkers - Origins and Formation of the Y Service* (Bletchley Park, 2000)

Philip McDougal    *The Chatham Dockyard Story* (Mersborough Books, 1981)

David T Hughes    *Sheerness Dockyard and Naval Garrison –* (Tempus Publishing Ltd, 2003)

Eric Millhouse    *Chronicle of St Upid* (Millhouse Beaumanor Staff Magazine, 1946)

Bryn Elliot    *Police Aviation History* (Elliot, 2004)

Russell Clarke    *The Secret Listeners* (BBC East, 1979)

Sinclair McKay    *The Secret Listeners* (Aurum, 2012)

*Kelly's Directory Rochester, Strood, Chatham and Gillingham, with Maps 1925* (Kelly, 1925)

R V Jones    *Reflections on Intelligence* (Mandarin, 1990)

## Other Sources of Information

The National Archive, Kew:
      HW3/33, HW3/92, HW14/2, HW14/3, HW14/4, HW14/6, HS1
Royal Navy Historic Branch, Portsmouth
Commanding Officerm HMS Excellent (Horsea Island)
Royal Engineers Museum, Brompton
Royal Signals Museum, Blandford
HM Prison Service
Radio Society of Great Britain
Marconi Archive (Bodleian Library, University of Oxford)
Commonwealth War Graves Commission
Dean of Rochester Cathedral
Royal Air Force Museum
Senior Naval Officer, Mumbai Dockyard, India
BAE Systems
The Headmaster, Kings School Rochester
Kent History Forum
London Gazette
Edinburgh Gazette
Kentish Gazette
Kent Messenger Group
1901 Census online
Bundesarchiv Koblenz
RCA of America
Hallicrafters of America
National Radio Corporation of America
Beale Family Archive
Malcolm Ellingworth (Ellingworth family records)
Paul Caton (Ellingworth family records)
Alex Beaumont (Ellingworth family records)
British Medical Journal (Payton Beale obituary)
Ken Carling (personal photographs)
Lt Col 'Sandy' Le Gassick MBE Royal Signals Rtd (anecdotal material)
Aubrey Stevens (Albert Stevens documents and photographs)
Robert Connolly (SLT Connolly RNR photograph)
Chris Barnes (anecdotal material)
Peter James (anecdotal material)
Bertram Ashman (anecdotal material)
Cynthia Adams (Pop Blundell photographs and anecdotal material)
Dr Philip Blenkinsop (Fort Bridgewoods photographs and anecdotal material)
Redvers Webber (anecdotal material)
Medway Archive Centre
Industrial Railway Society
Subterrania Britanica Collection

## Glossary of Terms

AAOR  Anti Aircraft Operations Room

ADI  Assistant Director of Intelligence

AM  Amplitude Modulaton

ARRL  American Radio Relay League

ATS  Auxillary Territorial Service (women's branch of the Army)

BBC  British Broadcasting Corporation

C  Head of the Secret Intelligence Service MI6

Cdr  Rank of Commander, Royal Navy

CQ  General call, used in telegraphy

CRR  Compilation and Records Room – Signals Intelligence

CW  Continuous Wave – Morse Code

DF  Direction Finding

DSM  Distinguished Service Medal

EWA  Experimental Wireless Assistant

Funkers  German Radio Operator

FANY  First Aid Nursing Yeomanry

GAF  German Air Force

GC&CS  Government Code and Cipher School (Now GCHQ)

GCHQ  Government Communications Head Quarters

GEC  General Electric Corporation

GHQ  General Head Quarters

GPO  General Post Office

HFDF  High Frequency Direction Finding

HQ  Head Quarters

KCMG  Knight Commander of St Michael and St George

KR  Urgent Message

HF  High Frequency

LT  Lieutenant Royal Navy or Army

LT CDR  Lieutenant Royal Navy

MBE  Member of the British Empire

MCW  Modulated Continuous Wave Morse Code

MI5  Secret Service

MI6  Secret Intelligence Service

MF  Medium Frequency

MFDF  Medium Frequency Direction Finding

OBE  Order of the British Empire

OC  Officer Commanding

OPGU  State Secret Police (Russia)

OPSIG  Operating Signal

OSA  Official Secrets Act (UK)

Q Code  Three letter groups used by telegraphists, all beginning with the letter Q. Each have a specific meaning, e.g. QRN = static interference

RAF  Royal Air Force

RN  Royal Navy

RNR  Royal Naval Reserve

RNVR  Royal Navy Volunteer Reserve

RSGB  Radio Society of Great Britain

RSME  Royal School of Military Engineering (Brompton, Gillingham, Kent)

SIGINT  Signals Intelligence

SIS  Secret Intelligence Service (MI6)

Sparkers  British term for a radio operator – from the days of spark transmitters

SRC  Sub Regional Centre

SSB  Single Side Band transmission mode. All power is placed into one sideband, with the other and the carrier being suppressed electronically

SWOPS  Special Wireless Operators (ATS Trade)

SYG  Special Y Group

TA  Territorial Army

VI  Voluntary Interceptor

VHF  Very High Frequency

VLF  Very Low Frequency

VR  Victoria Regina

WOYG  War Office Y Group

Y  Wireless Interception (when you sound the letters W and I together it sounds like 'Y')

Y Committee  Government body for coordinating Wireless Interception work